SIGNATURES
MIASMS AIDS
SPIRITUAL ASPECTS OF HOMEOPATHY

SIGNATURES MIASMS AIDS
SPIRITUAL ASPECTS OF HOMEOPATHY

MISHA NORLAND

with

CLAIRE ROBINSON

yondercott
press

Abergavenny, U.K.

Published in the U.K. by

yondercott
press

An imprint of Alternative Training Ltd.
Orchard House, Merthyr Road, Llanfoist, Abergavenny NP7 9LN, U.K.

Website: www.yondercottpress.com
E-mail: info@alternative-training.com

ISBN 0 9544766 0 3

British Library Cataloguing in Publishing Data

A catalogue record for this book is available from the British Library.

This book contains general information only. The authors accept no liability for injury, loss or damage to anyone acting on the contents of this book. No responsibility is accepted for any errors or omissions in the contents of this book.

Printed by Antony Rowe, Chippenham, U.K.
Cover design by Mani and Sam Norland
Cover artwork by Brigitte Norland
Typesetting by Betsy Levine

CONTENTS

PREFACE

Much of this book could have been written ten years ago—many of the ideas were in place. It has rested on the back boiler because I have been busy running the School of Homeopathy, teaching and being with my family—and also because for me, writing is an arduous task. Like many dyslexics who learn to write, I have compensated for lack of acumen by developing habits of perfectionism. I often rework a single sentence several times before I am satisfied. I disrupt my flow of ideas by concentrating upon details. When I speak, however, none of these impediments are apparent. For years, friends have suggested that I find a collaborator.

I am therefore grateful to Claire Robinson for working with me on this book. Claire shares my delight in finding the right words to clearly present what needs to be said and a fascination with homeopathy and philosophy. The latter stages of this book have been written in close collaboration; we have literally sat side by side and crafted the raw material of ideas and facts into coherent shape.

My thanks go to Stuart Gracie for his many years of management of the homeopathy correspondence course, alliance and friendship; also for taking on the publishing of this book. Without this implementation, it would still be languishing in a pending file.

I am grateful to Peter Fraser for his work on new provings and his substantial contribution to the AIDS and Falco peregrinus sections in the book.

I would like to thank Brigitte, my wife, for her painting (used on the cover) and for her ongoing support of me, our children, and our extended 'family': the teachers and students at the School of Homeopathy.

I would like to honour the memory of my mentor John Damonte who generously gave of himself and provided me with a vision of healing and homeopathy. Finally, my thanks go to E C Whitmont for his inspiration and encouragement. He was severe with me, entreating me to get off my butt and write a book incorporating the doctrine of signatures. "It is your duty," he said "to communicate your understanding!"

Misha Norland
2003

INTRODUCTION

Signatures, Miasms, AIDS shows how a deeper knowledge of two key concepts in homeopathic theory—miasms and the doctrine of signatures—can enrich our understanding of remedies and the states we encounter in our patients.

Part I presents some of the historical and alchemical background of homeopathy, placing this system of healing firmly within the context of the ancient, unchanging and eminently practical truths of the 'eternal philosophy'. In an Appendix, we show how an understanding of this knowledge gives a model for potency selection, based on observation of how vital energy expresses itself in individual patients. New light is cast on Hahnemann's original miasms of Psora, Sycosis and Syphilis, creating the foundation for an understanding of the 'newer' miasms posited by modern homeopaths.

Part II examines some polycrest remedies in the light of their signatures and miasmatic tendencies. The concept of signatures is expanded to include the origins, stories and myths surrounding the use of medicinal substances, as well as their cultural, commercial and scientific applications. Remedy pictures are underpinned by extensive clinical experience. Readers who are familiar with the journals *Homeopathic Links* and *The Homeopath* may be acquainted with some aspects of the remedy pictures, but these have been reworked to include new insights.

Part III looks in detail at the AIDS miasm through the nosode of that disease and the sarcode Falco peregrinus. New information is included from the provings of both remedies. Because these are new remedies, their materia medica 'pictures' are not established in the same way as those of the polycrests. The 'Natrum mur type' and the 'Silica type' have become familiar enough for us to fold our signature insights into the well-known remedy themes that have emerged from decades of clinical experience and evolving materia medica. But while Falco peregrinus and the AIDS nosode have been extensively proven and used curatively in some clinical cases, we cannot yet tell how the 'types' of these new remedies will present. Nor do we yet have a full clinical picture of the disease states that will respond to the remedies.

Our treatment of the AIDS nosode and Falco peregrinus in this book is therefore very different from that of the older polycrests. We present background information about the remedy substances, linking them to the themes that emerged from the provings. As these remedies are used by more homeopaths in future years, clearer pictures of the remedies will form themselves out of the raw material presented here, just as they have for the polycrests. However, in our experience, familiarity with the 'stories' of these remedies as presented in this book (in addition to repertory work and materia medica searches) has proved sufficient both to recognise corresponding disease states in patients and to bring about a curative response. We therefore thought it useful to include our existing knowledge in the hope that others will subsequently give it a more defined shape.

Part IV looks at the 'newer' Tubercular, Cancer and AIDS miasms within the context of a developmental model that helps us to locate patients and remedies on the miasmatic map, and also provides a summary of the developmental model of miasms used throughout the book.

Appendices include a model for potency selection based on an elemental model of constitutional types and a homeopathic glossary of commonly used terms for those who may not be familiar with all of the terms used in this book.

New provings carried out at the School of Homeopathy may be viewed in their entirety by logging onto www.homeopathyschool.com and linking through to the proving site provided by Peter Fraser.

PART I

SIGNATURES, MIASMS
AND THE ETERNAL
PHILOSOPHY

CHAPTER 1

THE DOCTRINE OF SIGNATURES

The doctrine of signatures holds that the Creator marked each of his creations with a sign. This sign or 'signature' was an indication of the healing property of the organism. Every ancient culture contains its own version of this doctrine, which was originally not just a medical principle, but a way of seeing the world. According to this world view, at the level of the dynamic life force or essence all things are interconnected. The same laws of nature that give form to plants, animals and minerals and their medicinal properties also give form to our bodies and the illnesses that take root in them. We cannot view a tree as just its fruits without taking into account its leaves, branches, trunk and roots, as well as the habitat in which it grows. It follows in the healing arts that by careful observation of the form, behaviour and habitat of a substance, we can learn how it interacts with our own bodies and minds.

Though there are allusions to the doctrine of signatures in the writings of the Greek physician Galen (AD 129–c. 210), it was first applied systematically to Western medicine by the great Swiss physician Paracelsus (1493–1541). Paracelsus was often referred to as the last alchemist and he was undoubtedly a forerunner of homeopathy, though it fell to Samuel Hahnemann, the founder of homeopathy, to codify and name it as such. Paracelsus said that our soul

> ...intuitively perceives the powers and virtues [of herbs], and recognises at once their signature. This signature is a certain organic or vital activity, giving to each natural object... a certain similarity with a certain condition produced by disease, and through which health may be restored in specific diseases of the diseased part.

> This signature is often expressed even in the exterior form of things, and by observing that form we may learn something in regard to their interior qualities even without using our interior sight. We see that the internal character of a man is

often expressed, even in the manner of his walking and the
sound of his voice. Likewise the hidden character of things is
to a certain extent expressed in their outward forms. As long
as man remained in a natural state he recognised the
signatures of things and knew their true character; but the
more he became captivated by illusive external appearances,
the more this power became lost.

Paracelsus' thoughts on signature were taken up by the German shoe-maker mystic Jacob Boehme (1575–1624). In the early years of the seventeenth century, Boehme had a series of divine revelations which inspired him to write a book, *The Signature of All Things*.

Boehme believed that the creator's "intent is to let you know the inward power and property by the outward sign; for nature has given marks and notes to everything, whereby it may be known". He called this system of signatures "the Language of Nature [*Natursprache*], which signifies for what everything is good and profitable". Boehme foreshadowed the homeopathic principle of similars, or 'like cures like', in his statement that "the outward life may be freed from sickness by its likeness". He further believed that the principle of similars revealed cures "not only for the body, but for the soul". Such curative similars could be found by close observation of signatures.*

For those who knew the Language of Nature, not only was the inward power of a thing similar to its outward form, but also its name was the same as the physical form. This was true because the entire created universe was continuously unfolding out of the infinite source in terms of speech or sound. The source of creation was silent but contained the entirety of all the diverse sounds and forms of creation in seed state. From this level, the name of each object or creature was brought into being. The name was understood as a network of subtle impulses or tendencies in which the entire structure of the physical form is contained in seed form, much as a great oak tree is contained in a tiny acorn or the adult form is contained within the germinal DNA.

Boehme believed the Language of Nature was the source of all other languages spoken by man, including the Latin and English tongues by

---

* Jacob Boehme, The Signature of All Things. London and New York: Dent, 1915

which we name plants, minerals and animals. To him, our term 'listening to the grass grow' and the seemingly poetic concept of 'the music of the spheres' would have been literally true, and not fanciful. He maintained that his ideas did not spring from theoretical speculation, but from direct cognition of the Language of Nature. His claim was borne out when some learned students tested him by taking him for a walk in the country and occasionally giving the wrong Latin name to a plant. In every case, Boehme, an uneducated man who knew little Latin or formal botany, intuitively knew which names were wrong because they did not match the signature.

The idea of name-form correspondence runs like a thread through history. The King James Bible's first text is "In the beginning was the Word, and the Word was with God, and the Word was God." The shamans, bards and wizards of ancient cultures *sang* objects and beings into existence. New Age thought has picked up on the traditional understanding that tells us to be careful of what we think and say, because thoughts are things and words are actions: that which we think and speak becomes our reality. The three wise monkeys' precept, 'see no evil, hear no evil, and speak no evil', echoes this principle.

Boehme's thoughts on signatures and the language of nature influenced the eighteenth-century Swedish mystic Emmanuel Swedenborg, whose works in turn were read by the renowned 19th century homeopath James Tyler Kent. By this route, these ideas entered mainstream homeopathic thinking, though they were implicit in the writings of Samuel Hahnemann. However, Hahnemann renounced the notion of signatures because he thought it simplistic. No doubt it had been used in a primitive and misleading manner, stating, for instance, that the shape of a particular seed indicated its correspondence to a particular bodily organ and on the basis of that alone, could be used to treat the diseased part. We agree that this is misleading and endeavour to rectify such misconceptions.

Both the doctrine of signatures and the Language of Nature deal with correspondences between apparently separate aspects of creation, where one aspect contains or evokes another. To recap, the doctrine of signatures says that by knowing the form of an object, we can know something of its medicinal use; the Language of Nature says that by knowing the name of

THE DOCTRINE OF SIGNATURES

an object, we can also know its form, and vice versa. This way of looking at the world is central to homeopathy, where we become used to thinking in terms of people being "Lycopodium types" or "in a Sepia state". We are simply saying that we perceive a correspondence between the person and the remedy picture.

Signature and symptoms

Knowledge of a remedy's signature is not merely a theoretical exercise that enables us to speculate about its homeopathic uses. The signature can give us a direct path through the myriad proving symptoms of that remedy. The provings are the records of symptoms that a remedy is capable of producing in a healthy person and which that remedy can cure in a sick person.

Bringing together all the symptoms of a proving into a cohesive remedy picture is often a challenge. As an example, why should a person needing Calcarea have fears about murder, fire and rats, and be worse from exertion? Looking at the remedy substance, Calcarea is made from the shell of an oyster. After passing through an immature mobile phase of existence, the oyster quickly transforms into a passive creature that sticks itself to a rock for the rest of its life. It is a filter feeder, taking in passing food particles, and relying upon its thickening shell for protection. Small wonder, then, that the creature, weighed down by its house, is useful for those who are worse for exertion. Calcarea types in health feel as safe as houses, while in sickness they feel as vulnerable as an oyster without its shell. Children in particular are wary of leaving the protective shell (their home). They may fear murder, because it endangers their own person; fire, because it endangers their house; and rats and vermin, because they invade their house and eat their food. In this way, the signature cuts through a remedy's many seemingly disconnected physical and mental symptoms to reveal the main themes and essence. Even if we don't accept the concept of signatures, they make excellent mnemonics to help us remember the 'shape' of a remedy.

CHAPTER 2

OUTER FORM AND INNER SPIRIT

Everything in creation, man and medicines included, has a visible and an invisible aspect, a limited outer form and an unbounded inner spirit. The outer form can be known by observation with our ordinary senses. The inner spirit can be sensed by intuition.

Many ancient systems of healing, including the Indian Ayurvedic system and the shamanistic traditions, stress the need to develop the powers of observation and intuition—the outward and inward eye—in order to get to know the visible and invisible aspects of medicinal substances.

Different cultures have different ways of training the inner eye of intuition. In Ayurveda, a traditional form of healing in India, the training of a physician involves living in the wilderness in the company of the plants and minerals that make up the Materia Medica. In meditation, the physician fuses his own awareness with that of the plant or substance and becomes one with it. In this way, he intuitively grasps the qualities and powers of the medicinal substance at first hand.

An example of intuitive knowledge from the European tradition is Dr Edward Bach, the doctor and homeopath who formulated his Bach Flower Essence system of healing in the early twentieth century. Dr Bach described how he went into the forest and meditated on a plant until it revealed its medicinal powers to him. Shamans use rhythmic drum-beats, chants, and herbs to induce altered states of consciousness in which they enter into the spirit of the medicinal plant or animal—both to learn its special power and to draw upon it for healing. Homeopaths, when they participate in provings, are following in the footsteps of these experts of intuitive knowing.

Direct intuitional experiences such as Dr Bach's are rarely recorded in present times. Even when they occur, they are not readily accepted by mainstream thinkers. For most of us, our outward eye is more valued and becomes our stronger faculty. However, the most complete knowledge is based on both inward and outward processes of perception. Traditional European herbalists, Ayurvedic and Chinese traditional physicians, and Native American healers and shamans, cultivate the habit of intuitional knowing as well as keen observation of the outer form of the medicinal substance. They train their senses to absorb as much as possible about the natural history, habitat, qualities, growth habits, taste, smell, feel and appearance of medicinal plants. The idea is to gather a full picture of the medicinal substance—its character—in order to match it to the picture of the patient's disease.

This is a vital process in homeopathy because it is based squarely on the law of similars, which states that a substance that causes a particular symptom in a healthy person will cure the same symptom in a sick person. In order to spot the remedy most similar to the patient's state at that time, we need to know the remedies as we know people, each with its own characteristics, habits and preferences.

Provings

In order to know the remedies from the inside and the outside, homeopaths underpin observation of the medicinal substances with knowledge of their provings. Provings were Hahnemann's brainchild. In a proving, a group of stable volunteers of both sexes are given a potentised dose or doses of the substance under enquiry. Usually, the provers do not know what the substance is. Over a period of time (usually about two months) and under supervision, they keep an on-going log of their altered state. They examine not only new and/or changed physical symptoms, but also mental and psychological symptoms. Provers are in effect the living instruments upon whom the melody of the medicinal substance is being played.

At the end of the proving, the logged information is gathered from all the volunteers and collated. During this process, it is established which symptoms are frequently, moderately, and least experienced. This organisation of symptoms constitutes the 'picture' of the healing agent. It is verified and enlarged upon by clinical experience.

Treating a person homeopathically is the opposite process to a proving. We give a sick person the remedy that would cause his symptoms in a healthy person, and the vital force is stimulated in reaction, with the result that his symptoms disappear.

The proving method of testing the characters of plants, animals and minerals in the laboratory of the human body puts homeopathy on a scientific basis, in that 'science' refers to knowledge that is systematic, repeatable and verifiable.

Materia Medica

The Materia Medica of homeopathy list the proving symptoms for that remedy, plus clinical observations of symptoms cured in people who have taken the remedy. Sometimes, if the remedy is made from a poison, toxicological symptoms are included, based on clinical observation of its victims. The symptoms gathered in the Materia Medica form the basis of the other main tool of homeopathy, the Repertory. In this book, we have quoted selected symptoms (rubrics, as they are called) to illustrate the essence of a remedy.

The Materia Medica has always expanded and continues to do so as new remedies are added to the homeopathic toolkit. The Repertory also expands to include the observations of new provers and the latest findings from clinical practice. Thus both the Materia Medica and the Repertory are storehouses of clinical experience—detailing the outward manifestations of the inner spirit of each remedy.

CHAPTER 3

THE HERMETIC TRADITION
AND HOMEOPATHIC PRINCIPLES

It is generally agreed that homeopathy is set upon three pillars:

- the law of similars;
- the potentisation of remedies and the minimum dose; and
- the working of the life force or *dynamis*. As Hahnemann writes, the life force in health "rules with unbounded sway and retains all parts of the organism in admirable, harmonious vital operation".

These three pillars are well-known in the hermetic tradition, so called after the famous alchemist Hermes Trismegistus, who was born in Thebes around 1399BC and who reportedly died in 1257BC. Hermes Trismegistus took his name from the Greek god Hermes, who presided over many qualities, including mischief (the unpredictable, the Joker in the pack). For this reason, Hermes' mother locked the little god in his room when he was only three days old. However, he transformed himself into a vapour, slipped under the door and re-formed himself on the other side. We derive our expression 'hermetically sealed', meaning a vapour-tight seal, from this story. The expression also carries the notion of a secret or sealed, hidden teaching. The hermetic tradition is also called the eternal philosophy, *philosophia perennis*. In the West it forms the basis of esotericism, kabbala, alchemy, theosophy, anthroposophy, astrology, and Jungian psychology.

The cardinal principles of the hermetic world view are the following:

- principle of unity;
- principle of correspondences or analogies;
- principle of polarity;
- principle of levels of consciousness or planes of existence.

Principle of unity

All things are related to the one—the ultimate level of existence. To achieve that unity and relatedness at a personal level is the higher purpose of our existence.

The eternal quest of science has been for a unified field theory that explains nature as a coherent whole. Physicists Isaac Newton and Albert Einstein spent the better part of their lives searching for a unifying theory and the mathematics to express it. The twentieth century has seen numerous conferences and high-level debates dedicated to the issue.

In homeopathy, the quest for unity is expressed by Hahnemann in aphorism 9 of the *Organon*.

> *In the healthy condition of man, the spiritual vital force is the dynamis that animates the material body, which rules with unbounded sway and retains all the parts of the organism in admirable, harmonious, vital operation, as regards both sensations and functions, so that our indwelling, reason-gifted mind can freely employ this living, healthy instrument for the higher purposes of our existence.*

This text directs our endeavours towards an unfoldment of Self, as the psychologist C G Jung would have expressed it. In terms of miasms, the drive to unity is the purest expression of the Psoric trend (see Chapter 4 on Psora).

Principle of correspondences or analogies

This principle expresses the similarity of form and function between microcosm and macrocosm, or little world/order and big world/order, often used to describe the little world of individual man reflected on a large scale in the great cosmos.

Another example is the spiral form which recurs throughout creation, in the growth of a shell or flower (microcosm) and in the wider universe as a galaxy (macrocosm). This spiral form is a universal shape described by the mathematics of growth. The first person to formulate this progression was the Italian mathematician Fibonacci. The Fibonacci series runs as follows: 1, 2, 3, 5, 8, 13, 21, 34, ... Each number in the series is derived by adding together the two previous numbers. This series describes the average population growth curve of rabbits and the way in which we heal (damaged cells are replaced according to this series). It determines the 'golden section', an aesthetically perfect proportion in classical architecture. In the golden section, as in spiral forms, the dynamic interplay of two forces, the expanding force of growth (outward thrust of the spiral) and the contracting force of self-referral (curving around the centre or source point of the spiral), is mirrored.

The principle of correspondences is beautifully expressed by the Romantic poet William Blake as "a universe in a grain of sand". Modern science uses correspondences in the form of models, for instance, molecular ball and rod models to show the construction of atoms, and computer modelling of subatomic events.

The idea of correspondence between heaven and earth was central to the alchemists. "As above, so below" is the primary statement of *The Emerald Tablet of Hermes,* a seminal text of the alchemical tradition:

That which is below is like unto that which is above and that which is above is like unto that which is below.

The alchemists used correspondences in their attempts to rectify their own internal nature through manipulating natural substances. For them, all forms of nature, inanimate and animate, had correspondences to the divine higher nature above us and within each of us. This formulation is similar to homeopathy, where the correspondence of inner disease and outer remedies brings about healing.

An alchemical myth tells that the emerald in the crown that Lucifer wore fell to earth when he was banished. This emerald is a synonym for the Philosopher's Stone, which in turn represents a power of transformation. Lucifer, literally, light-bearer, an embodiment of the sun, became Satan, who is associated with Saturn—the restrictor, the prisoner of the will. The metal that corresponds to Satan/Saturn is lead, while the metal that corresponds to the sun is gold. Turning lead into gold (the acknowledged quest of the alchemists) had a symbolic meaning which a study of astrology as well as homeopathic Materia Medica sheds light upon. Lead/Saturn, a force associated with contraction, slowing down, and stagnation may be transformed into gold/sun, a force associated with illumination and purpose. To put it another way, a power within us akin to Satan/lead may be redeemed (by inner and outer work) and transformed into a power akin to sun/gold. That which is below is like unto that which is above.

In homeopathy, the principle of correspondence is expressed as the law of similars, or 'like cures like'.

Principle of polarity

The manifested world involves duality: everything has its opposite. This principle is expressed by the ancient Chinese formulation of the Yin/Yang symbol. This depicts a circle in which there are two identical interlocking forms, like two whales—one is white, Yang; the other is black, Yin. In the dark of Yin there is a little spot of light, much as in the darkest night there are still stars to be seen. In the light of Yang there is a spot of darkness, like a solar spot on the surface of the sun or a black hole at the centre of a galaxy. These spots convey that each state contains the opposite state in seed or potential form.

Yin and Yang are in constant flux. Change is inevitable. According to Newton's Third Law of Thermodynamics, every action has an equal and opposite reaction.

In homeopathy, the polarity principle is expressed in Hahnemann's term, primary and secondary action. An understanding of this principle is crucial to homeopathic case-taking and analysis of case material, as well as in organising proving data and interpreting Materia Medica. This is because the diseased states of mind and body manifest in qualities whose opposites are always present, even if as yet unmanifest. They express as primary, uncompensated and secondary, compensated states. The uncompensated state is the one in which the disease first expresses itself. A compensated state involves the organism adapting in whatever way is necessary to ensure continued survival.

Medical science uses the concept of compensation to describe pathology. The terms 'uncompensated', 'compensated' and 'decompensated' are applied to heart disease. The uncompensated heart is operating well. An example of compensation might be the enlarged heart, which still fulfils its function, although the strategy is precarious. The decompensated heart is failing.

Homeopaths use these concepts to describe the development of pathology in remedies. For example: the uncompensated state of Nux vom is zealous, hard-working, determined although cramped. While in this situation, the patient would be unlikely to visit the practitioner, but he would be getting positive feedback from those around him. Nux vom, feeding off praise and innately driven, naturally tends to overstep his capacity. In order to sustain his over-zealous endeavour, he compensates by resorting to stimulants (wine, women and song, late nights and too much coffee and cocaine). At this stage of developing pathology, he may present with cramps, spasms or stomach ulcers. In the final stage, he decompensates; the flak of failure hits him in the face, and all he wants to do is find a quiet place for repose. However, he believes that he can't because somebody has sold his bed—a Nux vomica delusion.

In clinical practice, conscious and subconscious states seen in patients may also be interpreted as a complementary pair of opposites. This often plays out in dreams. For example, a dream of being a powerful giant may be an unconscious compensation for innate feelings of inadequacy. A dream of a grand house with ornate interiors (as revealed in the AIDS nosode proving) might be a compensation for feelings of being despised and rejected.

Kent pointed out that perversions of the affections, represented by the opposites of love and hate, are fundamental to a case. We would agree that fixity, or lack of fluency, at this formative level leads to disease. Aversion should be allowed to mutate to desire, and desire to aversion, in fluidic momentum to maintain psychological integrity. To put this into experiential terms, a healthy relationship between siblings, children and parents, and, indeed, life partners, allows for changing emotions. From a therapeutic angle, discerning any 'stuckness' at this energetic level is of maximum importance because it denotes the foundation of psychological as well as physical sickness. A stuck place is experienced by the patient in the body as a sensation (by one or more of the five senses), and in the mind as a memory and an image. This is the primary uncompensated state from which all later compensations generate. Recognising the *gestalt* or shape of this primary state is the key by which we unlock the case.

When a patient is given the simillimum, an initial intensification of presenting symptoms occurs because the symptoms of the disease are added to by the symptoms of the matching remedy. This is the primary action. Not infrequently, proving symptoms (additional to the disease) are experienced for a period of time. Subsequently, an equal and opposite reaction to that stimulus is initiated by the vital force—that which was up may go down, as with a see-saw. This is the secondary action. When we see these signs we expect a move into the opposite state of advancing cure, before the patient settles into a new balance. This new dynamically balanced state offers greater potential for change than was previously possible because it is a healthier, less stuck and less complicated, state than before.

Principle of levels of consciousness or planes of existence

In the ancient Vedic teaching of India, the generative Om—the 'Word' of the Bible, the first creative movement—gives rise to the three Gunas or qualities (the creative, destructive and balancing/maintaining principles). The Gunas in turn give rise to the five fundamental elements of earth, water, fire, air and ether/space.

The planes of existence are perfectly reflected in the Hindu system of Chakras. The lowest Chakra at the base of the spine represents foundation in earth; the highest at the crown of the head represents transcendence. The ancient Chinese wrote that the Tao (wholeness) gives rise to Yin and Yang and the five elements. The ancient Greek philosophers also wrote of the five elements. These ideas, which we have traditionally located in the classical Greek period, reach back to the Egyptian civilisation and before that to the Vedic civilisation. The library at Alexandria, which contained ancient books from India and the Middle East, was visited by Aristotle and others.

In homeopathy, three principal planes of existence are described as:

1. The spirit;
2. The dynamis, the instrument of the spirit or vital force, which directs all processes of the body;
3. The physical body.

The generation of potencies in an ascending series is based on refining the remedy substance from a more physical level to a more spiritual level.*

The principle of planes of existence also underpins the developmental model of the three basic miasms or inherited predispositions to disease (see Chapter 4 for a full explanation of miasms):

1. First miasm, Psora—disease of the skin, which, if suppressed, becomes the developmental platform for all further disease;

2. Second miasm, Sycosis—the infectious agent, the gonococcus, which inflames the mucous membranes before it penetrates more deeply into the organism, typically developing into rheumatism, warts and heart valve disease;

3. Third miasm, Syphilis—the infectious agent, the spirochete, which destroys the interior of the cell, eventually attacking the heart, the bones and central nervous system.

These are the three miasms described by Hahnemann. This triad is fundamental and sufficient for an understanding of the further miasms posited by us and other homeopaths:

4. Tubercular miasm—a mixture of Syphilis and Psora;

5. Cancer miasm—a mixture of Sycosis and Syphilis;

6. AIDS miasm—a mixture of Syphilis and Psora.

The concept of miasms as a progressive laying down of strata over time is supported by the historical observation that tuberculosis (famously a 19th century disease), cancer (which escalated rapidly in the 20th century), and AIDS (currently escalating, especially in Africa) have followed on each other's tails over the last 200 years.

---

* See Appendix 1: Model for potency selection

CHAPTER 4

MIASMS

Hahnemann describes miasms as inherited predispositions which allow disease to take root. Diseases are delayed, accelerated or modified in their progression by this inheritance. This theory is based upon the clinical observation that diseases leave their imprint (inherited predisposition) in the originally healthy soil of individuals. Their suffering, far from going to the grave with them and ending there, is passed on to future generations.

Miasms are laid down when someone succumbs to a disease and succeeds in suppressing its symptoms without quelling its source. This is generally accomplished by drugging. The disease is suppressed, but does not disappear. It is driven deeper within the organism, only to weaken the constitution and that of any children, and so on down the line of inheritance. The sickness remains in the soil. To continue the analogy: a farmer may leave a record in the soil for the future by depleting the land by over-intensive use or poisoning it with agricultural chemicals. Conversely, by improving the soil, fewer diseases will be passed on to future generations.

Hahnemann felt that acute diseases were relatively easy to deal with. The prescriber had simply to find the substance which produced similar symptoms to the diseased state in a healthy individual and, after administering the potentised similar remedy, cure would occur rapidly and completely.

However, treating chronic diseases was often a different matter.

Between 1810 and 1816, after Hahnemann had published the first editions of the *Organon,* he realised that though many patients responded well to their initial remedy, some returned with a new complaint or a relapse of the old one. He sought an answer to this perplexing problem, and surmised that the difficulty lay in a deeper disease underlying the immediate problem. In his book *Chronic Diseases,* he explained that in a chronic case, the physician:

> *... has not only to combat the disease presented before his eyes, but that he has always to encounter some separate fragment of a more deep-seated original disease. He, therefore, must first find out as far as possible the whole extent of all the accidents and symptoms belonging to the unknown primitive malady before he can hope to discover one or more medicines which may homeopathically cover the whole of the original disease.*

For twelve years, Hahnemann looked for an insight into this hidden weakness in man. In 1827, he felt he had found the answer. He wrote:

> *I discovered ... that the obstacle to cure of many cases ... seemed very often to lie in a former eruption of itch, which was not infrequently confessed, and the beginning of all subsequent sufferings usually dated from that time ... after careful inquiry it usually turned out that little traces of it (small pustules of itch, herpes, etc.) had shown themselves with them, from time to time, even if but rarely as an indubitable sign of a former infection of this kind.*

Hahnemann believed that the original disease, Psora, the 'itch', formed the soil into which other diseases implanted themselves. He concluded that chronic diseases were built upon an inherited substratum of constitutional weakness or degeneration—the miasms. In addition to Psora, Hahnemann identified two further miasms, Sycosis and Syphilis, which were built upon the fundamental Psoric layer. James Tyler Kent, writing in the 19th century, was the first homeopath to connect the Sycotic figwart disease with suppressed gonorrhoea. The Syphilitic miasm derives from suppressed or hereditary taints of that age-old scourge, syphilis.

The soil

When analysing any case, the miasms underpin the present, predominating and persistent symptoms. Using the analogy of plants, the type of plant that grows in any area reveals the nature of the soil. Buttercups reveal a water-logged soil, sundews a peaty soil, and windflowers a sandy soil. The individual expresses the predisposition for disease (soil) by the symptoms of the disease (plant). The miasm is not the disease itself, but it is the soil in which the disease grows. It is worth remembering that Louis Pasteur, who founded modern medicine's notion that much disease is caused by pathogenic micro-organisms, recanted. His dying words are said to have been: "It is the soil that is all-important, not the disease."

The word 'miasm' derives from the Greek for rut or furrow, the implication being that the person becomes stuck in a rut grooved into present time by past action. Of the miasms, Psora is the oldest and most grooved into the substratum of our collective being. Over the centuries, it has been suppressed by application of medicated creams, such as calamine and hydrocortisone. Such suppression robs the Psoric trait of its primary physiological outlet. The disease is driven deeper and attacks internal organs of greater importance. For cure to occur, the suppressed eruption must re-appear during treatment. Only then will there be relief of the internal trouble.

Since suppression has been the norm for so long, primary Psora has become perverted, giving rise to the multiplicity of symptoms and diseases we see around us today. Not only is suppression medical, it is also societal, in the form of moral, religious, and political conventions, and in this form predates the advent of doctoring.

There is dispute among homeopaths about whether miasms exist, and whether they are confined to Hahnemann's three. Later homeopaths have suggested additional miasms, such as the Tubercular and Cancer miasms. This has opened a debate as to whether these are truly separate miasms or merely combinations of Hahnemann's three. What is certain is that an understanding of the three original miasms lays the groundwork for an understanding of additional miasms posited by later homeopaths. This book explores a developmental model, which includes Tuberculosis, Cancer and AIDS miasms, where each miasm lays down a subsoil in which a newer miasm takes root.

Psora, the Hydra-headed mother of disease

In *Chronic Diseases,* Hahnemann called Psora "the oldest and most Hydra-headed of all the chronic miasmatic diseases". He explains:

> *Psora is that most ancient, most universal, most destructive, and yet most misapprehended chronic miasmatic disease. For many thousands of years it has disfigured and tortured mankind. During the last centuries it has become the mother of all the thousands of incredibly various (acute and) chronic (non-venereal) diseases, by which the whole civilized human race on the inhabited globe is being more and more afflicted.*

> *Psora is the oldest miasmatic chronic disease known to us ... and therefore not to be extinguished before the last breath of the longest human life, unless it is thoroughly cured, since not even the most robust constitution is able to destroy and extinguish it by its own proper strength.*

Why is Psora so difficult to eradicate? To answer this question, we need to go back to basics and consider the nature of creation.

From the perspective of unity, all creation is an act of separation or division from the one. In the foetus, the myriad cells develop by division from the one original fertilised egg. In humans, individual consciousness begins with the emergence of the 'I' or ego. The 'I' separates itself, divides itself off, from the original unity of mother and child.

Why does this happen? In other words, what is the point of diversity when unity is, as mystics throughout the ages have confirmed, bliss?

In the original unified state preceding creation, there was no way for unity to know itself. To do this, it had to experience something other than itself. 'I' had to draw a boundary between what is 'I' and what is 'not-I'—what is 'this' in here and what is 'that' out there. From a human perspective, it could be stated that this drive to know 'I' explains the evolution of consciousness. It is for this reason that we refer to our species as *Homo sapiens*—the human who knows.

We can see this individualising process in any child as it grows to adulthood. The baby learns that it is distinct from its mother. That is, it develops memory—a *gestalt* of image, smell, touch—upon which it can draw when it is separated from its mother. As it becomes more independent, it learns to put greater distance between itself and its family. An adolescent may feel a growing sense of separation from peers. For the duration of adult life, most individuals continue to work out what sets them apart from the rest of the world, drawing and re-drawing boundaries between the 'I' and the 'not-I'.

With the birth of 'I', the one has become two: the 'I' and the 'not-I'. The 'I' is the subject of perception, the one who sees; the 'not-I' is the object of perception, the thing that is seen. The relationship between the subject and object makes three, the third being the process of observation itself.

These three principles form the origin of divine trinities in religions, such as Father, Son and Holy Ghost or the three Gunas or qualities (the creative, destructive and balancing/maintaining qualities). They also form the basis of tri-miasmatic analysis:

- 'I' defines itself by attachments, by possessing attributes and things = Sycotic miasm;
- 'not-I' represents the pole of detachment from attributes and things through destructive processes = Syphilitic miasm;
- The process of observation involves feelings of separation and isolation = Psoric miasm. Persons with such feelings seek healing through re-establishing a sense of unity. They do this, mistakenly, by defining themselves and developing more and more attachments to things. Thus we go round the cycle again. This 'wheel of illusion' is referred to by the Buddha in his Fire Sermon, to be discussed later in this chapter.

The infinite relationships between these three fundamental principles of creation weave the web of life, giving rise to all forms, just as the three primary colours give rise to all colours. Each form or colour, though apparently separate, is in essence just a part of the whole, just as individual waves on an ocean are nothing but the ocean. But when individual beings forget their unified source and identify themselves predominantly with themselves as separate beings, then Psora (separation), Sycosis (attachment) and Syphilis (destruction) are born.

The illusion of separateness is viewed in all mystical traditions as a delusion, or ignorance of the true unity. The Sanskrit term for this Psoric state of delusion, *pragyaparat,* has been translated as 'the mistake of the discriminating faculty', since it is this faculty which creates separation between the 'I' and the 'not-I'. The delusional state can be experienced on many levels: physical, emotional, imaginative, and spiritual. It could also be said that Psora is 'the mistake of the heart', for the heart represents the unifying principle.

It is no accident that Psora, the itch, is a disease of the skin, which is the dividing membrane between 'I' and 'not-I'.

To heal Psora, then, is no less than to cure the basic delusion around which the created universe revolves—that of separation and division. Such a cure is the goal of all religions since the beginning of time. The word 'religion' derives from the Latin meaning to bind back (to the source). Mystical traditions aim at enabling adherents to directly experience at-oneness with the unified source of creation, and thus to hold in their awareness the unity beyond the ever-changing world of duality. The world of duality is represented by the miasms of Sycosis (desire) and Syphilis (aversion). It is an elusive goal, and failure to attain it has given rise to the concept of sin. The Greek word for sin was *hamartia,* an archery term meaning 'missing the target'. In this light, it is easy to see why the concept of original sin—the sin that everyone has been born with since the Fall of Man—took root in Christianity. Just as it is impossible to eradicate original sin from humankind, so it is impossible completely to eradicate Psora.

Psora and the Biblical myth of the expulsion from Eden

Many religions describe man's fall from innocent unity into self-awareness and beyond—the world of space and time, change, death and suffering, separation from God and ensnarement by delusion.

In the Christian tradition, the story of the genesis of the separate ego, the birth of Psora, is told in the biblical story of the Fall, the expulsion from the Garden of Eden.

When first created by God, Adam and Eve lived peaceably with the animals and knew no fear; nor did the beasts dread man, for in the continuum of existence there was no division. Psychologically, Adam and Eve were still in the early childhood realm of at-oneness.

The apple of the tree of knowledge bestowed the capacity for choice, for knowing good from evil. This may be interpreted as the birth of conscience, or simply as discriminative intelligence. From the perspective of the evolution of the species, there may have been a moment when the capacity of the mind for thought was great enough to allow this quantum leap to occur. The development of the frontal cerebral lobes distinguishes man from the higher primates and may mark the physical prerequisite for the development of the ego and associated functions such as conscience.

At this point in evolution, instinctive behaviour, which does not know good from evil, became modified by reason. Past experiences could be scrutinised, analysed and compared, offering a choice of responses to situations. When Adam and Eve ate the fruit of the tree of knowledge of good and evil, they effectively stole this attribute of God. As a result, God banished them from the garden (of childhood innocence), in order to ensure that the fruit of the other tree, the apples of immortality, remained safe.

The story of the Garden of Eden, like all stories, operates within a context of place and time. Yet it refers to an eternal process. Adam and Eve before the fall can be viewed as existing in an eternal state of simple consciousness which underlies and creates complex awareness and the many forms of creation. After the fall, Adam and Eve lose awareness of the unity in which they were created. Instead of effortlessly gathering the foods that nature offers they now must toil for their living and till the soil amongst the thistles. Division between Adam and Eve, and enmity between man and beast, appears. Suffering, in the form of labour pains, is born. The Psoric state, marked by lack, struggle, insufficiency, alienation and longing for reunion, comes into being.

The origin of Psora

Hahnemann states that Psora is the most infectious of all chronic miasms—far more so than the other two miasms, Syphilis and Sycosis. He explains that for infection with Syphilis and Sycosis to occur, there must be a certain amount of friction in the most tender parts of the body, the genitals, which are richly endowed with nerves. The vagina and the urethral outlet at the glans of the penis are muco-cutaneous borders where the inside and outside of the body meet. Alternatively, the infectious agent must touch a wounded spot. But the miasm of the itch needs only to touch the general skin, especially with young children. Hahnemann writes that it is communicated so easily that the physician, feeling the pulse of one patient after another, has unconsciously transmitted the infection. Often a baby is infected while passing through the birth canal of a mother infected with the disease; or the baby receives the infection from the hand of the midwife.

Hahnemann believed that after contact, contagion expressed itself in primary external manifestation on the skin. The general health of the individual would not deteriorate as long as the skin eruption remained. The person's quality of life would depend on internal factors such as strength of constitution, and external factors such as nutrition and environmental stress.

Over the centuries, the general health of mankind has deteriorated, with more problems on deeper levels of the organism. Hahnemann attributed this deterioration to the suppression of superficial symptoms. The vitality has become so suppressed that it is difficult for Psoric individuals to throw off diseases and their waste products.

Hahnemann believed that grief was the greatest arouser of latent Psora, and that other triggers included dirty living conditions and poverty.

Central to a Psoric's mental state is the sense of having lost out, a sense of unrest and abandonment, a feeling of waiting for something to come and redeem them. Of course, they do not know what this may be. Arising out of this state of waiting is a constant sense of anxiety. But this anxiety rarely motivates the Psoric into activity. A variant of the Psoric state, with a Sycotic coloration, may give an impression of speed. This anxiety-driven, hurried state is a veneer to hide inner uncertainty. Commonly, the anxiety expresses itself through the extensions of the central nervous system to the skin. The itch is an expression of this.

The Psoric person is an introvert. C G Jung defined an introvert as a person who meets situations with an inward and unexpressed "No". (Conversely, an extrovert meets situations with a wholehearted "Yes".) One type of Psoric behaviour may appear overtly confident, giving the impression of optimism, yet closer enquiry will reveal this to be a cover-up. Psoric people are uncertain about their place in the world. They often express themselves hesitantly and are slow in movements and mind. Uncompensated Psora is the least colourful, the drabbest miasm, while compensations include displays of bravura and boasting.

Psoric's comprehension is often profound, though gradual and plodding. They must study hard to retain and assimilate facts, but through hard work, they eventually remember their lessons well. Commonly there are fears of failure: "I can't do it. Why should I bother trying, because whatever I do is doomed to fail?" Associated with this is the fear that they will always remain poor, will not be able to make the grade, and will not be able to provide for their families. As a result they may become hoarding and miserly. At the opposite pole of Psora is the person who is wedded to hope, addicted to faith, and certain that the universe will provide.

Other characteristic features are a slow metabolic rate and lack of vital heat, wounds that are slow to heal, and a tendency to dry skin and skin eruptions.

The origin of Sycosis and Syphilis

The word "Sycosis" comes from the Greek word for fig, after the fig-warts that gonorrhoea tends to produce in the genital area.

According to Kent, Sycosis results from a past gonorrhoeal infection, either in the patient themselves (primary infection) or transmitted from parents and grandparents (secondary infection). The primary infection is characterised by a thick greenish or yellowish discharge from the point of contact, usually the genitals. The discharge is attended by burning which is frequently worse during urination because the mucous membranes lining the urethra are inflamed.

The Sycotic miasm—initiated, according to Kent, by both primary and secondary routes of infection—is typified by discharges from mucous membranes, cellular overactivity, growths, moles, warts and excrescences. Such people are often a human barometer, worse for any change in the weather and developing rheumatic complaints.

Syphilis is the result of contagion by the spirochete bacterium, which enters the cell and destroys it. Typical characteristics of the disease include necrosis, bloody discharges, ulceration and degeneration. The Syphilitic miasm manifests in physical and emotional destructiveness.

Not everyone who becomes infected with gonorrhoea or syphilis will pass on a Sycotic or Syphilitic miasm. Much depends on how the disease was treated, as well as the vitality of the patient. The best outcome, of course, is that the acute disease and chronic miasmatic state are treated homeopathically. The worst outcome is that the disease is suppressed or simply left untreated. In this case, genetic changes occur and the miasm is passed on to any children.

Miasms and the Buddha's Fire Sermon

Miasms can be identified from their outward disease manifestations, but they also exist as pre-formative disturbances at the dynamic centre of a person's being. These disturbances link well with the Buddha's teaching known as the Fire Sermon, in which the Buddha identifies three fundamental causes of suffering or "the three fires": desire (attachment), aversion, and illusion (ignorance).

Hahnemann was almost certainly unfamiliar with the Buddha's teachings. However, it is no surprise that great souls looking at the territory of human suffering would come up with similar maps. Psora is characterised by illusion and ignorance of the essential unity of life. The Psoric is hounded by feelings of separation and isolation. Sycosis is associated with desire which, when sustained, manifests as greed. Syphilis is characterised by anger and aversion which, when sustained, manifests as hatred.

In the Fire Sermon, the Buddha said, "Your house is on fire, burns with three fires." Fire destroys, purifies, and cauterises. Traditional astrology and C G Jung associate the fiery element with creative impulse, intuition and sexual passion—qualities that rise up unexpectedly and forcibly. Fire combines two basic life-giving qualities: light and heat. This is why fire is an archetypal symbol of Godhead. Upon the sacred altar, torches or candles burn. The three fires of greed, aversion/hatred and isolation are negative aspects of this energy. They keep us removed from the positive aspect of fire, burning in the hell realms where destructive forces hold sway over creative impulses.

Healing the individual in essence means turning the energy of the fires around so that that which has been negative becomes positive. This can be seen as reducing the inherent miasmatic background, enabling the individual to better realise their potential and express their innate divinity—God indwelling, from which unconditional love radiates to all beings.

The Fire of Psora

The most difficult of the three fires to comprehend is illusion or ignorance. This is because of the fact that ignorance, the delusion that we are separate from the rest of creation, arises directly from ego. Because we identify ourselves with ego, we do not wish to let go of it.

When ego is born, it naturally begins to regard itself. In the beginning this process is instinctive, and linked to survival drives. The cry of the baby for food, love and warmth becomes transformed into the cry of the child, "I want". We witness the birth of the 'I' with a capital letter, separate from the wholeness and from unconditional love.

Another way of understanding this illusion of separation is to see the great, primordial, undefined space of the formless being filled with activity—the individual activity of the ego. This may be seen as the ego spontaneously dancing, an activity born, quite innocently, of life itself. In so doing, the ego creates individual space, boxes in universal space, fences in territories. These enclosures are like rooms in which the individual now believes that he resides. The way we define ourselves becomes so linked to the bounded activities that occur in this room that in time we begin to believe that it exists. We identify with, and feel that we are, the bounded activity itself and not the unbounded dance of life. Out of this limitation arises anxiety. This illusion is very powerful and holds sway over the lives of most people most of the time.

This illusory state is synonymous with the Psoric state of ill health, which, according to Hahnemann, we all share. The sensation of separation, which is basic Psora, is the ground state of primordial fear itself. Imagine the fear of the child who is separated from mother, home and security.

The process of separation is re-enacted with every birth. It has been reinforced in modern times by surgical and medical procedures employing severe mechanical techniques. In the delivery ward under bright lights, the baby is born into the gloved hands of the gowned doctor. Immediately the cord is cut and tied, the baby held by her feet, mucus is drained from her throat and nose by pipette, and she is measured and weighed. Finally, terrified and screaming, she is returned to the partly anaesthetised mother.

The Fires of Syphilis and Sycosis

Fear initiates the fight-or-flight mechanisms with which we are all familiar. Aggressive behaviour is commonly found in frightened individuals, a fact recognised by animal behaviourists and psychotherapists. This psychological posture is characterised by the projection of fear upon an object, which, when sustained, leads to hatred. This state is synonymous with the Syphilitic miasm.

Another aspect of separation is loneliness, longing and neediness. This posture is characterised by clinging and wanting, which, when sustained, leads to greed. This state is synonymous with the Sycotic miasm.

The Buddha taught that next to illusion, desire and aversion are fundamental sources of suffering. Excessive desire becomes greed and leads us to want more than we can use. Over-use leads to depletion of resources, which in turn leads to the feeling of lack characteristic of Psora. This in turn leads to the feeling of hatred of other people, seen as competitors for the insufficient resources—a hatred characteristic of Syphilis. The resulting excessive aversion leads to fear and greed for the things that make us feel secure. We become tied into a knot of terror and violence.

Near the hovel of Psora are the edifices of the twins, desire (Sycosis) and aversion (Syphilis). Desire likes a grand lifestyle, a large and luxurious dwelling, while aversion lives in a tall, well-defended tower. These twins have an irresistible affinity for each other, a love-hate relationship.

We are all susceptible to these reaction patterns, which, when exaggerated and sustained, are the roots of the miasms. We move towards that which we like and away from that which we dislike. We ride on a giddy see-saw of emotions and reactions. If we look closely, we can reduce all our baser feelings to the two fundamental states of desire and aversion. Our appetite for food operates in a similar way, as does all bestial behaviour. The entire animal kingdom is ruled by these two states. In a simple form, so are plants, whose reactions towards and away from a stimulus are known as tropisms.

The Psoric's basic posture is: "I cannot have; I cannot do; I cannot be"; the Sycotic's is: "I must have; I must do; I must be"; the Syphilitic's is: "I must attack before I am destroyed".

The Sycotic type

The key idea of Sycosis is more and more life. The state is typified by greed and a compensatory stance of shame and covering up. Sycotics want to widen their vision to include more and more. The result is proliferation on both physical and mental levels.

These types feel hurried. They sense that there is not enough time for them to acquire all the things they desire; life is too short. They are seekers after things; it matters not whether these things are experiences, ideas, concepts, '-isms', '-osophies', food, sexual partners, power, or money. Sycotics feel they must have more and may be compulsively driven to acquire status. They tend to aggrandize themselves. They are extravagant in their costume and gestures, and boastful in their speech.

Because of the conflict that arises between conscience and their boastful, extravagant nature, they characteristically develop a profound sense of guilt, which may express itself in the form of the projection typical of the Sycotic: fear of supernatural phenomena. In end-stage pathology these people feel that they are being watched, that there is something 'out there' telling them what to do or criticising them. The Sycotic's state is more obsessive than the simple fear of ghosts or of the dark characteristic of the Psoric nature. It becomes an idea as fixed as a fig-wart fixed to a muco-cutaneous border, an obsession.

The physical expression of the Sycotic miasm tends towards a fast metabolic rate, resulting in a warmer constitution than that typical of the Psoric. Mucous membranes are a common seat of trouble: catarrh is the Sycotic's bane, as is rheumatism (the word is derived from the Greek *rheuma,* river). The typical discharge is bland or muco-purulent. They tend to produce tumours, polyps, fibroma and condylomata, but are unlikely to have a malignant cancerous predisposition unless the Syphilitic miasm is also well marked.

Typically, Sycotics are much worse for damp or living in humid atmospheric conditions. This hydrogenoid (worse for water) constitution is the result of an outer sensitivity built upon inner susceptibility to water. They are water-logged within, their constitution being characterised by the over-production of mucus. On the physical level, this is a consequence of the effort of the vital force to exteriorise the taint of primary or inherited gonorrhoeal contagion. Gonorrhoea first makes itself known by a discharge of pus.

Examples of the Sycotic miasm are provided by the Thuja, Pulsatilla and Rhus tox remedy pictures in later chapters of this book. (Thuja also exhibits AIDS miasm characteristics, while Rhus tox exhibits AIDS and Tubercular miasm traits.)

The Syphilitic type

The key idea in Syphilis is less and less life. As sustained aversion leads to hatred, the focus narrows to include less. An image comes to mind of a predator, with focused destructive intention. Syphilitics have a single-minded purpose, a type of tunnel vision. The intention is focused upon one object only, so that less is seen. The periphery is secondary. The conclusion of such a process, as the qualities of life are removed one by one, is death.

The flipside of the Syphilitic ability to focus in to a point is creativity—focusing inspiration into expression.

Perversion and destruction are keynotes of the Syphilitic miasm. Syphilitic people can be filled with the deepest feelings of rancour and the most destructive hatred. Their motto is that they will kill or be killed. The posture is one of terror, which may immobilise, and/or attack. If the aggression/anger is unexpressed it may turn inward and transform into suicidal depression.

Other emotional expressions are jealousy (a contraction of space—there's only enough room for you and me), suspicion (an emotion shared with Sycotics), and resentment. Given the venereal and necrotic nature of the miasm, it is no surprise that their fears are of dirt, disease and contagion. They fear that people will attack them. They may have dreams of attack, war and firing squads, and of corpses and decay. These people believe that the world is not just passively hostile (as does the Psoric), but actively hostile, out to get them. They may become obsessively superstitious in order to "protect" themselves from evil influences. The posture of the Syphilitic is that of a rat against a wall fighting for its life, or suicidal depression and longing for death.

Their metabolic rate is fast and typically, they are hot people. They may describe a feeling of "boiling inside" and "as if steam is escaping through the pores of the skin". However, as they begin to return to health and approach a more Psoric state, they may experience cold-blooded states. Bodily processes are necrotic: should there be ulceration, it will tend to spread rather than heal. Psoric ulcers might also be slow to heal but this is because of indolence. The Syphilitic ulcer will destroy surrounding tissues, and be bloody and painful.

Children born with a Syphilitic inheritance may have peg teeth. They may suffer from backwardness or epileptic seizures, these symptoms being directly related to the degeneration of the central nervous system. A history of alcoholism and drug abuse is not uncommon. Syphilitics are much worse for heat and their pains are greatly aggravated at night. The pains of the Syphilitic tend to be insupportable. The headache often feels as if the head were in a vice, crushing the bones.

In later chapters of this book, examples of the Syphilitic miasm are provided by Mercurius, Lachesis, Tarentula and Falco peregrinus remedy pictures. Falco also exhibits AIDS and Tubercular miasm characteristics. We would also refer readers to Jeremy Sherr's book, *Dynamic Materia Medica—Syphilis.*

Where we describe a remedy in terms of more than one miasm, we mean that the remedy is a mixture of these miasms, with the first-mentioned miasm dominant. For example, "Psoro-Sycotic" means that the remedy represents both Psora and Sycosis, with Psora dominant.

While the 'newer' Tubercular, Cancer and AIDS miasms can be described in terms of Hahnemann's three miasms, they also have their own discrete identities which we later delineate. For example, while the AIDS miasm can be seen as a combination of Syphilitic and Psoric miasms, it also brings its own distinct characteristics.

CHAPTER 5

MIASMS IN CLINICAL PRACTICE

Hahnemann felt that when taking a case, a true totality of symptoms must include a recognition of the active miasm at that point in time. He advised careful study of each of the chronic miasms in all their stages of development so that their characteristic features could be recognised in a patient. The 19th century homeopath J H Allen concurred:

> We cannot select the most similar remedy unless we understand the phenomena of the acting and basic miasms, for the true simillimum is always based on the existing basic miasms, whether we are conscious of it or not. It is necessary for us to know in detail about the chronic miasms as sometimes it is not sufficient if we follow the totality of symptoms and select the most similar remedy. We cannot in fact select the most similar remedy unless we understand and utilise the phenomena of the uppermost, the acting miasm, as this represents an integral part of the totality.

Most cases nowadays consist of mixed miasms, but we usually find one miasm uppermost and that particular miasm should be given priority when considering the totality of symptoms.

Prescribing methodologies

The prescribing methodology we espouse is that of the single remedy, the simillimum, allowing it to act until it no longer furnishes curative results. The idea is to find the remedy that matches the deepest level of disturbance within the patient. This is the uncompensated expression of the disease from which all other states emerge—that is, all compensations in the patient's entire case. By "entire case" we mean the etiology as well as present symptoms. An analogy made popular by Ibsen in *Peer Gynt* is that of the onion—layer by layer, the onion may be peeled, eventually revealing the growing tip in the centre. (In *Peer Gynt* the growing tip turned out to be no-thing, a truly Psoric outcome!) In the homeopathic model of layers, the growing tip represents the past, including the miasmatic disturbance, and the outer layers represent the development of the pathology over time.

There is, of course, another way of revealing the growing tip of the onion. This is to chop the onion in half, using the sharp knife of skilfully directed inquiry. In this case, the entire structure of the onion is revealed, including the growing tip at the centre. In other words, the uncompensated state, miasm, and all subsequent developments are displayed.

Both these models, both ways of revealing the onion, are relevant to practice. We espouse the 'chopping in half' methodology, because in theory at least, it provides us with a direct trajectory to the simillimum. This remedy has the greatest capacity to take our patient upon a journey towards health. The simillimum also may be employed for any occasional acutes that arise. By definition, the simillimum is capable of turning any disorder into order.

However, it is not always possible to discover the simillimum. The quest has been compared to finding the Holy Grail! In such cases, the 'layers of the onion' model is the one which we (wittingly or unwittingly) apply. It is sometimes the case that the remedy we had thought was the simillimum works only after an 'uncovering' or intercurrent prescription has been made. An intercurrent prescription refers to a second, and occasionally even third, remedy given in between doses of the identified simillimum. Some practitioners teach that these intercurrent prescriptions are usually the nosodes, on the grounds that such prescriptions deal with the miasms directly. This has not been borne out in our practice, although it was taught to us from the very beginning and we have had plenty of time to try it out. Sometimes, especially in young children and in end-stage pathology, the nosodes work, and sometimes, more frequently, it is other remedies which act to unscramble the case. In other words, 'uncovering' remedies do exist, but they are not always nosodes.

In order to find the simillimum, we have no need to make a miasmatic diagnosis as such; we simply apply the law of similars. The surest way of getting on track is to help our patients discover their uncompensated state through the right kind of case-receiving. However, a working knowledge of the miasmatic background helps us appreciate what is happening in a patient, and this in turn helps us select those particular symptoms and signs which are most characteristic at any given moment.

Viewing a case through a miasmatic looking glass reveals the overall trend of pathology. It is as though the miasm takes hold of the patient's inherent nature and the vital force through which it expresses itself, and distorts it. It is this distortion which miasmatic analysis reveals. Those symptoms which are not part of this thrust, of this characteristic miasmatic distortion, can be placed into second rank, while those which are characteristic are placed in first rank. This allows us to more accurately select rubrics for repertorisation. When it comes to differential analysis, an appreciation of the miasmatic coloration of individual remedies helps us select the better 'fit'.

Most people have all of the three basic miasmatic tendencies, although these may manifest as layers. From clinical observation, many cases resolve themselves as if one layer is removed at a time, thus revealing a deeper underlying state. This lower stratum may in turn reveal a yet more subterranean layer. Layers can alternate. We may see-saw between Syphilitic, Sycotic and Psoric remedies for some time before moving towards those which are settled into a more purely Psoric domain. By moving patients in a Psoric direction, we are moving them to a level of greater health. This is so because the Psoric miasm is basic, the *terra firma* of imbalances. Harking back to the teaching of the three fires as described by the Buddha, we recall that the state of illusion or ignorance, when healed, leads to bliss because there is no longer any sense of separation, anxiety, or fear of want.

Elizabeth Wright Hubbard warns us not to go too deep too soon, by which she means that we should approach the interior economy of our patients with respectful caution. Many of our European colleagues, especially those operating within the medical framework, agree. They go further and recommend the use of 'drainage remedies' to support weak organs and de-tox before approaching the hallowed ground of potentised remedies, let alone the simillimum.

Wright Hubbard also speaks of not blowing the fuse with too high a surge of power. We fully agree with this. While she is not advocating a model of layers, she is cautioning us with regard to potency. We must match the remedy to the symptoms, and the potency to the patient's constitutional elemental type* and prevailing miasmatic predisposition. The degree of miasmatic loading is directly proportional to the pathologising (see *Organon,* Aphorisms 201–206). Higher miasmatic loading indicates a lower potency. Lower miasmatic loading indicates a higher potency.

Having established a framework for miasmatic analysis, we can apply the theory to all remedies. We can see Psora in Calcarea, Sulphur, Lycopodium, Psorinum, Natrum mur and Silica; Syphilis in Aurum, Mercurius, the Iodides, Nitric acid and Syphilinum; and Sycosis in Medorrhinum, Thuja, Rhus tox, and Pulsatilla.

However, while one miasm is always dominant, all remedies are more or less coloured by two or three miasms. For instance, while Sulphur is the greatest anti-Psoric remedy in the Materia Medica, it also involves the other miasms. We know this from a breakdown of its symptoms into miasmatic categories.

As examples of miasmic mixtures in remedies, Silica is pre-eminently Psoric, yet has a dash of the Syphilitic miasm. Mercurius is Syphilitic, with a considerable Sycotic aspect and a hint of Psora. Argentum nitricum is both Syphilitic and Sycotic with a dash of Psora. Should we describe someone as, say, a Sycotic type, we must bear in mind that we are in fact describing a Syco-Psoric constitution, for it is impossible for either Sycosis or Syphilis to manifest in isolation without Psora. Should there be a strong Syphilitic tendency in a patient, then the remedies selected will be Syphilo-Psoric.

Thinking of miasms when treating patients is valuable because it takes us deeper and makes us look more closely at the hierarchy of symptoms and at the causative levels of disease. It helps us find the basic underlying patterns which rule an individual's life through inheritance—the pattern of the past as it manifests in the present.

---

* See Appendix 1: Model for potency selection

Predispositions for diseases

Many authors and prescribers, ourselves included, suggest that a disease contracted yet suppressed in childhood may result in a susceptibility to that disease process in later life. Alternatively, it may give rise to a modified symptom development which can be traced back etiologically to the suppressed illness. Such disease susceptibility can also be passed on to an unborn child from ancestors who suppressed the original disease.

This notion has been extended to include inoculation and drug miasms. The homeopath Eugenio Candegabe stresses the importance of prebirth "patterning", as do psychotherapists. Rajan Sankaran extends the notion of inheritance to include parental experiences that are unresolved at the time of the child's conception. These form the roots of future disease manifestation. Sankaran has formulated these ideas into an elegant system with multiple miasmatic categories. These observations, while being clinically valuable, use the concept of miasm in a manner that is not compatible with Hahnemann's generalised definition. Sankaran's formulation of miasms is more specific in detail and relates to the individual's manner of response to stimuli. This is described in his book, *The System of Homeopathy,* and is recapitulated in *An Insight into Plants*. Sankaran's map of miasms describes the pace, depth and desperation to which a sensation—the uncompensated state—is experienced.

Miasms and disease types

Whilst certain characteristic disease types are underpinned by miasmatic states, it is important not to think of specific diseases as belonging to any particular miasm. All miasms can manoeuvre the body into expressing any pathological state. For instance, eczema is not necessarily a purely Psoric disease, for the Sycotic miasm will add its influence, resulting in a tendency towards purulence, while the Syphilitic miasm would add a tendency towards necrosis.

In cancer (a disease which arises out of "the marriage of the three miasms", as Elizabeth Wright-Hubbard remarked), the Psoric individual will tend to produce indolent growths and metastasis will be delayed. The Sycotic will tend towards rapidly developing, massive and infiltrating cancers, with death being caused by obstruction. The Syphilitic will tend towards necrotic cancers resulting in a painful death.

Childhood diseases

It is not only chronic disease that is underpinned by the miasmatic load carried by the patient. Miasms belong to the collective inheritance of the race and are expressed as such by children in the form of childhood diseases. As is well evident, the surfacing of childhood diseases, so long as their development is not attended by long-term sequelae, is characterised by a developmental leap. For instance, the Psorically backward child begins to speak; the angry, tantruming Syphilitic child becomes calmer.

Rudolph Steiner held that incarnation was a gradual process from conception until maturation. He believed that acute fevers, such as those at the onset of childhood diseases, represent a state of physical flux within the tissues of the body, a breakdown of structure similar to that which occurs in the chrysalis during the pupating phase of the caterpillar prior to the emergence of the butterfly. It is during this physical flux that the energy of the incarnating spirit is best able to mould the cellular structure in its image. Thus childhood diseases are intimately associated with the process of healthy maturation. Modern medicine has established that the uninoculated vanquishing of childhood diseases helps the immune system to mature. It has been suggested, with good supporting evidence, that interference in this process by immunisation is associated with an increased incidence of auto-immune diseases. This view is vindicated by almost a century of experience on the part of homeopaths.

From the miasmatic point of view, measles is primarily a Psoric manifestation, though its sequelae, such as middle ear infections and gummy eye problems, have a Sycotic origin. Scarlet fever combines Psoric with Syphilitic traits; the disease can be very violent, resulting in rapid death. Chicken pox is primarily Psoric and corresponds to Hahnemann's description of that miasm, in that it involves itching vesicles. However, the Psoric miasm combines with Sycosis, as is evidenced by the common usage of Rhus tox for the eruptive stage of the disease and the characteristic aching restlessness. Sycotic/Syphilitic remedies may also come into play, such as Mercurius and Antimonium tartaricum. German measles is primarily Psoric. Whooping cough is dependent upon a "soil" composed of all three miasms.

Because inoculation inhibits or distorts the primary (often Psoric) manifestation of childhood diseases, it interferes with the natural tendency of the body to throw out miasmatic tendencies. In other words, the practice is suppressive. The pay-off is chronic disease in place of acute disease.

PART II

SIGNATURES AND MIASMS
IN POLYCREST REMEDIES

CHAPTER 6

SULPHUR—VOLCANIC FORCE

A predominantly Psoric remedy

Sulphur is the first in the trio of anti-Psoric remedies, followed by Calcarea and Lycopodium.

Sulphur comes from deep within the earth. Volcanic activity heats sulphur-bearing ores, breaking them down so that liberated sulphur ascends as a vapour with other sulphurated gases to the highest reaches of the stratosphere. Sulphur is found also in yellow crystal form around volcanic vents or fumaroles, where the heated gas has cooled and sublimated, and in liquid form in active volcanoes.

After major volcanic events, weather patterns are disrupted for years, due to the sunlight-blocking effect of particles in the upper reaches of the earth's atmosphere. When a volcano is actively erupting, then gaseous sulphur makes the connection between earth below and the atmosphere above.

Above and below

The remedy Sulphur has to do with the connection from below (earth) to above (spirit) and its reverse, and with a person's ability to make those connections. Because homeopathic remedies act out in polarities, Sulphur comes into play where a person is unable to integrate the worldly with the spiritual. The central issue is a dialectic comprising of the elements of idea and form, impulse and actuation, thinking about it and doing it.

At the spiritual end of the polarity, with his head in the clouds, we find a typical Sulphur type, the ragged philosopher. He is an intellectual, and burns with high-minded ideas, plans and philosophies. His problem is that he cannot bring his theories or philosophies "in the air" down to earth. He cannot realise them in a concrete form or talk about them in a way that is comprehensible.

He can be actively anti-materialistic. He despises things that are valued and coveted by most of society, and values things that most would despise ("delusion, rags are as fine as silk"). He may dress in the same tattered jacket and carry the same battered briefcase for twenty years. He thinks that his ancient briefcase cannot be bettered, and even if a better one was available, he cannot see the point of buying a new thing when the old one still holds up. It is characteristically Sulphur-like (delusions of wealth as well as delusions of being poor) that the Chancellor of the Exchequer appeared on budget day with a scuffed old case. In recent years, the old briefcase has been replaced.

Some Sulphurs may be well-dressed, but will betray themselves by wearing odd socks or a tie stained from falling in the soup. The upside of Sulphur's anti-materialism is that he may see an inner beauty in people and things that others miss. In India, even today, holy sadhus conform to this Sulphur image.

The Sulphur type who most often features in homeopathic writings is the high-minded artist or scientist who is hopelessly impractical and cannot bring what is above down to earth. But there is another Sulphur type who embodies the opposite polarity: an earth-bound stranger to spiritual life, concerned only with the material and physical level of reality. He may even be mentally dull. His heavy, rough physique will reflect his earthiness.

Another earth-bound Sulphur type is the aggressive business person, preoccupied with making money and accumulating material possessions. These people still bear the Sulphur stamp of being poor actuators. They pay the price in feelings of inferiority and fears of poverty while covering up and compensating by delusions of wealth and self-aggrandisement.

The above-below theme is also seen on the level of mental and physical symptoms. Sulphur has ascending effects such as rushes of blood and flushes of heat. He fears heights and, if driven to despair, may commit suicide by throwing himself from a high place.

Sulphur and the ground

Standing is the worst possible position for Sulphur. Every standing position is uncomfortable for him and aggravates his complaints. His temperament too makes it difficult for him to be static for long. He feels discomfort in the soles of his feet, the part of the body that connects with the earth. They may burn at night so that he has to stick them out of the bedclothes. These symptoms express the unease which Sulphur feels towards being earthed.

Sulphur symbology

The dual nature of the Sulphur personality—the ungrounded spiritual side and the grosser, earth-bound material side—is clearly seen in the historical view of the element.

Sulphur's grosser aspect has made its way into Christian symbology. The traditional English word for the element was brimstone, or burning stone. Brimstone came from deep within the earth and appeared around volcanoes and hot springs, seen as entrances to the underworld. Because of this, and because it smelt bad, it was a short leap of the imagination to make the element a vital ingredient of hell.

Certainly, the literature of hell and its devils is a wonderful source for Sulphurous homeopathic rubrics of both gross and spiritual polarities. Readers of William Blake's *Marriage of Heaven and Hell* or John Milton's *Paradise Lost* will recognise the egoistic, idealistic, ambitious, passionate, creative Sulphur type in the character of Satan. Both poets portrayed Satan as a rebellious, iconoclastic destroyer of the status quo, a fiery purifier of a stagnant hierarchy who strives heroically but futilely to outreach God and offers godlike qualities to man—once again, the Sulphur theme of trying to connect above with below.

Traditionally, in his attempt to marry heaven and earth, Satan is unsuccessful because his ego, his sense of 'I'-ness, gets in the way and perpetuates the tragic sense of separation. A common Sulphur theme is ego getting in the way of connection with others. This manifests in the form of selfishness, dictatorial behaviour and a feeling that because his idea or way of doing things is superior, he does not have to listen to others.

The Satans of literature are surrounded with the sulphurous colours of red, black and yellow. When heated, yellow sulphur turns red and finally black. In homeopathy, we see these colours in Sulphur's mental rubrics like a feeling that she is dirty ("delusion, she is black") and physical symptoms like red face or yellow deposits on the skin. Sulphur often suffers from liver problems, which can lead to a yellowish complexion.

The double nature of sulphur—its affinity with the depths of the earth and the heights of spirituality—was recognised by the alchemists. To them, sulphur embodied the double nature of man: the one, crude, dirty and evil-smelling, the black corrupter and ruiner of the great spiritual work; the other, the spiritual principle, the purifier, bringer of light and life. The alchemists associated sulphur with the aggressive, outward-directed masculine principle and with the sun. Sulphur was made stable by mixing with the feminine principle, symbolised in alchemy by salt and the balancing principle of mercury.

Evil smelling versus purifying

Satan and his fellow devils were thought to betray themselves by the whiff of sulphur they brought with them. The Sulphur type is known for his foul-smelling discharges: flatulence, perspiration, halitosis and faeces have the characteristic sulphurous 'bad eggs' smell.

As well as being the evil-smelling one, sulphur is also the purifier, burning up contagion and impurities. Sulphur's purifying qualities led to its use in agricultural chemicals like pesticides and fungicides, developed to 'clean up' the messier elements of nature. It is ironic that the use of these substances has led to the pollution of our soil and water. The purifier has turned into its opposite of the filthy one.

Sulphur's purifying reputation gave it a central position in traditional allopathic medicine, where it was routinely prescribed in spring to clear out the congestions of winter. Sulphur often has a spring aggravation, at a time when the whole of nature is bursting forth in the same centrifugal manner as volcanic sulphur. Sulphur drugs were the forerunners of antibiotics and are still used where the latter fail, as well as in the primary treatment of certain diseases.

Homeopathically, Sulphur the purifier is indicated in constitutions prone to problems of stagnation: slow circulation, delayed elimination, and insufficient oxygen in the cells. It is also used to balance Sulphur types who are stuck in the opposite state of overactive purification that is characterised by increased circulation, inflammations, hyper-sensitivity, exaggerated oxidation and combustion (for example, ravenous appetite) and tissue breakdown. In this polarity, it is as if Sulphur were burning himself up.

Sulphur and water

Sulphur hates bathing; perhaps he fears that the very act would put out his fire. And what fire there is—and what intense itching! The skin burns ten times worse after bathing. This, in part, is the reason why these types hate washing and gain a reputation for dirtiness and foul smell. Yet suicidal Sulphur, desiring extinction, may choose drowning as the method. At the opposite polarity to Sulphur's hydrophobia, we find his extreme thirst. He can gulp down large amounts of cold water to cool his overheated body.

The burning stone

As we might expect with a remedy made from the burning stone, Sulphur has many symptoms around heat. He is worse from becoming overheated, so he is aggravated at 11am, as the sun gets higher in the sky, and at night from the warmth of the bed. He may have burning sensations anywhere in the body, but especially at the crown of the head and the soles of the feet, which links back to the above-below theme. The bodily discharges—faeces, urine, and coryza—also burn, and leave the surrounding skin red and sore.

From inside out

Sulphur the substance and Sulphur the remedy share a centrifugal theme, of things coming from the inside out. This process occurs in a typically volcanic way, with much violence, heat, and burning. The discharge outlets of the body such as nose, mouth, ears, anus, and urethra can be compared to the vents and fumaroles of the volcano, and the Sulphur patient may show reddening and burning around these orifices. There is a tendency to skin eruptions like boils, cysts, suppurations, styes, and swellings, all accompanied by burning. Sulphur is also prone to yellow crusty skin irritations around the orifices, mirroring the yellow crusty deposits of sublimating Sulphur vapour around the volcanic vents. Temperamentally, too, Sulphur is fiery and irritable, with a tendency to erupt in sudden anger. But he tends not to bear grudges, and his anger abates as quickly as it arose.

Since Sulphur's centrifugal path is also the path of homeopathic cure, there has been a tradition among some homeopaths (though the practice is questioned by others, ourselves included) of routinely prescribing Sulphur in unclear cases to bring out hidden symptoms.

Suppression

The silliest thing one could ever do with a volcano would be to try to cap it, though this has been tried at least once in this century, with devastating consequences. Similarly, the Sulphur patient does not respond well to suppression, which drives the ailment in deeper and makes him more seriously sick. The Sulphur child with eczema, if treated with hydrocortisone cream, may quickly develop diarrhoea, asthma or hay fever, or anti-social behaviour.

Connecting

A major industrial use of sulphur is in vulcanising latex. When sulphur is boiled with latex from rubber trees, it creates an extremely strong and elastic material. The sulphur binds the naturally weak latex together, much as in making custard and cakes, sulphur-rich egg yolks are used to bind the ingredients together. Indeed, many protein molecules bind together into macromolecules using sulphur as the 'glue'. This binding quality of sulphur is due to its chemical reactivity—its ability to form double and multiple bonds. Indeed, it is seldom found in its pure form because it readily combines with other substances. It is only when sulphur compounds in the earth's crust are broken down in volcanic regions that sulphurous gasses issue forth.

We can see from sulphur's binding and combining properties that the Sulphur person is much concerned (or not concerned at all) with relationships and partnerships. A common problem is that they cannot form proper relationships because they are too egoistic, domineering and selfish. As Catherine Coulter points out, the person who holds forth in a long monologue about himself and promptly falls asleep when someone else starts talking probably needs Sulphur.

Sulphur's failure to make and maintain relationships may lead to his feeling disappointed in his friends ("ailments from deceived friendship") and desire to live alone ("aversion, to all persons"). Sulphur can feel unappreciated because other people do not attach importance to his ideas, which appear quite wonderful to him—a manifestation of his tendency to think rags as beautiful as silk.

Sulphur and Psora

Hahnemann called Sulphur "the king of anti-Psorics". It is significant that Sulphur suffers many skin eruptions, as skin forms the boundary between the 'I' and the 'not-I'. Sulphur particularly endures eruptions, redness and itching at muco-cutaneous borders, as this is where the inside meets the outside. These symptoms represent primal suffering on the physical plane of the nascent Psoric miasm.

Summing up, the two main themes of Sulphur are:

- connecting (and in pathology, not connecting) from above to below; and
- connecting (and not connecting) horizontally with others.

Thus Sulphur in the pathological state cannot earth lofty ideas or glue together human relationships.

CHAPTER 7

CALCAREA CARBONICUM—
THE PROTECTIVE SHELL

A predominantly Psoric remedy

Calcarea is the second in the trio of anti-Psoric remedies, being preceded by Sulphur and followed by Lycopodium. As Sulphur is associated with the fiery beginnings of creation, so Calcarea is associated with early oceans from the Silurian right through to the Cretaceous periods. The atmosphere then was much as it is now: bacterial evolution had created an oxygenated platform for the evolution of plant-life and photosynthesis. The carbon cycle was well underway. The oceans dominated the earth and seaweeds, diatoms, molluscs and corals prevailed. The great limestone deposits that form substantial parts of the earth's crust or skeleton were being laid down.

Limestone is formed by the deposition over millennia of the calcareous skeletons of marine creatures, including oysters. Crushed limestone, when heated in a furnace, produces quicklime. Quicklime plus sand and water forms a soft mortar which hardens over time into stone-like cement. This has been used for thousands of years in the construction of dwellings, to stick together stones or bricks or as a material in its own right. The theme of softness and the protection afforded by a home is central to the remedy picture of Calcarea.

The remedy Calcarea is made from part of the shell of the bivalve mollusc, the oyster. Molluscs are primitive invertebrates—filter feeding, flabby creatures with no backbone. Their skeleton is on the outside of their bodies in the form of the shell. This matter is stratified in alternating soft calcium carbonate and dense pearl-like layers. The remedy is made from the soft matter. Some species of oyster can live for hundreds of years, during which time their shell may become a foot thick. They are sessile, passive creatures.

The shell

The theme of the shell and passivity are at the centre of this remedy. Evolved for protection against the thundering surf (Calcarea has the delusion that her body is being dashed to pieces), the oyster's shell keeps what is inside, in, and what is outside, out—the Psoric note.

For the Calcarea patient, the theme of the shell translates as the home and the early cradling of safety that is necessary for the infant. Infancy is the time when at the physical level of being, calcium metabolism is most likely to be awry, and when at the psychological level, uncertainties and fears crop up. This is the time when the remedy Calcarea has its greatest place. This softness and passive vulnerability characterises Calcarea patients' state, whether they are young or old. The central issue is a dialectic between the elements of flabbiness and solidity, fear and endurance, stay-at-home safety and go-get-it daring.

The child or adult who needs Calcarea has trouble assimilating calcium salts. They may crave eggs and children may eat calcium-rich lime, plaster and cement. Often, these children cannot tolerate milk or are put onto formula milk, which does not give them what they need either physically or (because they may be deprived of breast or skin contact) psychologically. Thereafter, they lack a sense of being wanted, of safety and belonging.

On the physical level, calcium salts are incorporated in bone, solidifying and adding structure to the organism. A failure to assimilate calcium translates as a tendency to be flabby, as an oyster without its shell. The Calcarea child's bones are soft like the soft strata of the oyster's shell, weak and rickety. The fontanelles take too long to close. Margaret Tyler remarked that Calcarea types are characterised by tissue "of plus quantity and minus quality". An adult's handshake may be limp and clammy, the 'wet fish' handshake. There is general physical and mental weakness, often to the extent that the person feels they cannot overcome lethargy, dullness and confusion of mind. They cannot focus their intention upon a difficult task, preferring to remain in a state of inertia—passive, secure, maybe in bed surrounded by soft toys. Because the Calcarea person feels unprotected from outside influences (without an adequate shell), he develops a compensatory self-protective habit. He prefers to stay at home where outer security protects inner vulnerability.

Mentally, too, he feels insecure and over-sensitive. He cannot bear to hear horrible and sad stories, because such things affect him profoundly. He suffers greatly from criticism, and finds it difficult to shake off the resultant feelings of being misunderstood or that he is plain slow-witted. He has many fears, usually low-key and lurking and almost impossible to get rid of. Once an image, an idea, a concept, grabs hold of the imagination of a Calcarea type it persists obstinately. A positive side to this is good long-term memory, the 'elephant mind'; while a negative aspect might be persistent and recurring unwanted or even homicidal thoughts.

Cemented to a rock

Once the oyster has reached maturity, it cements itself to a rock with the intention of staying put forever. Calcarea children and adults commonly experience dizziness and terror of heights, of ascending and of falling. A Calcarea girl will be content in the secure home of her parents. She may hesitate to marry and leave, but if she does, she will want to recreate that feeling of childhood protection in her marriage. She will be happiest when surrounded by close friends and family and will resist change and newcomers. She may not go out much and will not be the type to seek adventure, although an occasional escapade is a possibility, including, surprisingly, sexual adventure. This is so because the over cautious inner state must sometimes find its outer compensation in thrills and spills.

Mentally, Calcarea feels as weak and easily exhausted as he does physically. He is slow to catch onto things. The child will sit out of the way in the back of the classroom. At worst he cannot concentrate at all and feels powerless to overcome the feeling of sluggishness or paralysis of the brain. Just as the oyster, cemented to a rock, is powerless to manoeuvre out of the way of threats, so questions directed at him are perceived as threatening. Answering them may require a spontaneity he does not posses. He will do well enough at an exam, though, given plenty of time for revision and provided the question is within the realm of his swotted-up knowledge. Just as the oyster relies on its shell for protection, so the person needing Calcarea prefers to stay at home, away from threatening public places where people may observe his confusion or criticise him.

Calcarea's dreams and delusions may involve murder, fire and rats—all of which threaten his self-protective shell. He fears that his protectors may be killed, his home burnt down, and his food supply eaten by vermin.

Filter-feeders

Oysters are filter-feeders. The shell opens to reveal rows of little hairs that beat to waft a vortex in the ocean around them. This brings all manner of small organisms into the shell that are filtered and sorted. The Calcarea child sits quietly and absorbs everything; he takes it all in and lets little of himself out. As he grows older and begins to suffer from his receptivity, or if he hits a sudden crisis point, he may become excessively selective about what he takes in, leading to the over-cautious behaviour, obstinacy and conservatism for which Calcarea types are renowned.

The pearl

Oysters endeavour to keep out external irritants by means of their protective shell. But if they cannot keep these irritants out, then they will encapsulate them in a pearl. They do this by slowly building up layer upon layer of glistening hard calcium carbonate. None of the softness of the malleable layers of the pappy shell goes into the production of the pearl! This remedy has an affinity with all the tissues in the body that incorporate pearl-like, white fibrous connective tissue. A healthy individual deals with tuberculosis by encapsulating the tubercles in white fibrous connective tissue to render them dormant. However, a patient with Calcarea constitutional tendencies will not be able to do this and, typically, will succumb to the disease unless potentised remedies such as Calcarea are given.

In his lecture on Hepar sulph, Kent wrote that he would rather be in a room full of razor-slashing murderers than put himself in the hands of a dangerous prescriber of high potencies. He particularly mentioned Silica, Hepar sulph and Sulphur as remedies that will break open encapsulated tubercles. This can be lethal, as the patient may rapidly die of TB.

Interestingly, the sharp grain of sand which commonly gets inside the oyster shell and which seeds so many pearls is made largely of silica. (One of the themes of those needing homeopathic Silica is 'can't get it out'.) Kent advises a dose of potentised Calcarea to stimulate the body's encapsulating mechanisms.

Aquatic environment

Because oysters live in the sea, it should come as no surprise that Calcarea affects the movement of body fluids. The slightest exertion makes the Calcarea person perspire; he suffers from night sweats and coryza; and is aggravated by moist air. Sweats tend to occur at the back of the neck, and to smell sour. The Calcarea male may suffer from too-frequent seminal emissions. The Calcarea woman may have milky leucorrhoea, or produce too much milk.

Processes involving obstruction of flow—coagulation, hardening and calcification—are also affected by Calcarea, including swelling of breasts before menses, and swollen or hardened glands.

Belladonna: the acute of Calcarea carbonicum

In the treatment of small children, Calcarea and Belladonna are the most common chronic and acute remedies, respectively. Calcarea is the chronic subsoil for its acute, Belladonna, to the extent that Belladonna (deadly nightshade) will only grow in chalky soil. An image for Belladonna is that of a person running away from a pursuing tiger: active, blood pumping, a flight for survival. There are high fevers and wild hallucinations—the opposite of Calcarea's chilly indolence. The Calcarea-Belladonna relationship highlights the dynamic of chronic and acute states beautifully. The one is too much at rest, and the other overcompensates with too much activity.

Symbology and astrology

Just as Sulphur is associated with the fiery masculine force of the beginning of creation, symbolised by the sun, Calcarea is associated with the feminine, receptive aspect of creation, symbolised by the moon. Even today, this dual symbology may be seen in the radiance that sits on the altar in the Catholic church, which shows a sun made of golden rays and a moon made of pearls.

In astrology, the moon rules the feminine water sign of Cancer. Cancer is characterised by receptivity and sensitivity, and rules the home—a direct correlation with the vulnerable Calcarea person seeking security in her shell. The main gemstone associated with Cancer and the moon is the pearl. Calcarea types often have an aggravation leading up to or at the full moon. Women may notice an aggravation before the menses, when retained fluid builds up in the breasts and lower abdomen.

Pearls of wisdom

At the soul level of being, Calcarea inclines the individual towards slow and thorough introspection. This may develop into a pearl of wisdom. It is common for the older Calcarea child to go to church and to research religious teachings. This is not done in a flighty Sulphur speculative way, but in the form of an ethical, moral and practical evaluation. It is the innate sensitivity to horrible things, to dangers, to the threat to security from war, which motivates this enquiry.

Many religions use pearls to symbolise the junction point between this world of change and immortality. Christianity has the pearly gates that lead into heaven. Hinduism has the 'blue pearl' or *bindu* point. This is the 'smaller-than-the-smallest' gateway located in man's consciousness through which his awareness must pass in meditation in order to reach pure consciousness or infinity, 'larger-than-the-largest'. The awareness can only do so when it is unshackled by the psychic baggage of the external world. This is why this internal journey traditionally requires sustained discipline, a focused awareness, and a sure aim. The Bible talks of the eye of the needle leading to the Kingdom of God, through which a camel may more readily pass than the rich man (baggage-laden awareness). This idea is echoed in the statement: "Strait [narrow] is the gate and hard is the path that leadeth unto life, and those who find it are few."

If its signature and symbology are heeded, then the highest application of Calcarea may be to create the structure which will enable a person to reside in wisdom. As pointed out, the shell keeps in what is inside, and keeps out what is outside. Thus the oyster shell remedy helps remove the Psoric delusion of the separation of inside and outside: it allows the two to be simultaneously in the same place, at the junction point between this world and immortality. This in turn allows a realised state of wisdom to be born and extended into the outer world.

CHAPTER 8

LYCOPODIUM CLAVATUM—POWER AND COWARDICE

A predominantly Psoric remedy

Today, Lycopodium clavatum is a tiny creeping club moss. But during the Carboniferous era, it was a massive structure over 150 feet in height. Even now, its basic form is tree-like.

This massive evolutionary shrinkage translates to the level of the Lycopodium individual as an uncertainty about whether he is big, powerful and successful or tiny, insignificant and a failure. Both polarities are found in the Repertory. On one hand there are rubrics such as "dictatorial"; "domineering"; "command, talking with air of"; "power, love of". On the other hand there is "confidence, want of self"; "discouraged"; "cowardice", and "Fear of appearing in public". He fears undertaking new things because he does not feel up to the task, though, ever conscious of his public image, he would not like to admit this.

It has been postulated that Lycopodium plants grew large because of the high concentrations of carbon dioxide from volcanoes in the atmosphere during the Carboniferous era. As the amount of carbon dioxide decreased, the Lycopodiums became smaller, until they reached their present size.

However, as they decreased in size, they continued to colonise vast tracts of land. There are few places on earth where Lycopodiums cannot be found. They have adapted to suit different climates. For example, in the cool northern temperate zone, the gametophyte, the part of the plant that makes reproductive cells, grows under the insulating surface of the ground, whereas the tropical Lycopodiums grow their gametophytes above ground.

In terms of plants, Lycopodium is one of the most successful members of the vegetable kingdom. In human terms, the central issue faced by Lycopodium types is that the terrain to be colonised is vast, that they must succeed in colonising it, yet that they feel inadequate to the task. Lycopodium's polarity is one of love of power and fear of failure or cowardice.

Vascular system

From the point of view of early plants, the trick of success was to get water onto dry land, so that dry land could be colonised. The plants that had the edge were the ones to develop a vascular system that could take up and transport water. The first plants to do this were the Lycopodiums and their relatives.

A tree's trunk and branches are made up of a supporting woody central section called the xylem and a softer vascular section around the outside, called the phloem, which draws up water and nutrients. Lycopodium doesn't have a xylem and a phloem; its stems are entirely made up of vascular tissue. This system is more primitive as well as less rigid than that of the more evolved trees. In the person who needs Lycopodium, the assimilative and eliminative functions of the digestive system and the kidneys are weak. In later stages of pathology, the mind also becomes weak. The mind and memory represent a higher octave of the digestive and eliminative functions: digestion, assimilation, retention and rejection occur at both levels.

Primary and secondary action in Lycopodium

In the light of Hahnemann's exposition of primary and secondary action, there is debate as to which of Lycopodium's polarities—love of power or the feeling of powerlessness—is the primary action, and which is the secondary action or compensation.

Most homeopaths say that cowardice represents the uncompensated state and love of power is its natural compensation. But we could turn the argument around and say that the sense of magnificence, achievement, and power, persisting in Lycopodium's memory from the time when it was a giant, comes first; failure, stemming from Lycopodium's subsequent shrinkage, comes second. In the modern age, it is ingrained in the human psyche that God is huge and we are poor grovelling creatures, tiny and inferior. The dream in Lycopodium that contains this idea is that of being surrounded by giants.

But debating this question may be as circular a process as asking which came first, the chicken or the egg. It is possible that primary and secondary actions (uncompensated and compensated states) each contain the seed of the other, just as, in Chinese philosophy, Yin (feminine) contains the seed of Yang (masculine). In this case, love of power and powerlessness would be two coexisting sides of the same coin. This is consistent with the nature of duality: pleasure is never found without pain, and happiness cannot be known without unhappiness. Following this thread into the Lycopodium psyche, Lycopodium would not desire power unless he knew what it was to feel powerless, and he would not know the meaning of powerlessness unless he also knew what power felt like.

In our search for the source of Lycopodium's pathology, we could question what quality underpins these states. We would suggest that Lycopodium's fundamental pathological function is a shrinking and withering away— like the erection of an impotent man. In other words, shrinking and withering represent the bodily sensations as well as the feeling and the mental expression of Lycopodium's downside. Obviously, these qualities will be brought to the practitioner to be cured, rather than a love of power.

Finally, it is less important to know whether cowardice or love of power is the primary state than to recognise that a patient needing Lycopodium is as likely to present with extreme lack of confidence as in the stereotypically bossy mode.

Spores

Lycopodium spores are extremely light. They rise high on the slightest gust of wind and travel great distances, thus colonising land more effectively. These characteristics correlate with several Lycopodium personality traits. The Lycopodium person easily rises to the top of his profession, achieving social or intellectual eminence. Lycopodium types are often found in positions of great responsibility, as head of a school, college, or business.

Such positions frequently carry with them the need to perform, to rise to the occasion and project an impressive image ("likes-a-podium!" as the homeopath David Mundy expresses it). Performance is the field in which Lycopodium excels; yet it is also the bane of his life ("timidity, appearing, to talk in public, but capable to"). He will deliver a brilliant speech or presentation, catching fire and illuminating the occasion just as the fatty Lycopodium spore burns with a brief, bright flame; the spores have been used as a flash powder to illuminate a photographer's image. But this process is at great cost to himself. Before the event, Lycopodium suffers ailments from anticipation, such as digestive disorders. After the event, he may burn out and collapse with prostration of mind, mental exhaustion, and brain-fag.

With Lycopodium's urge to take on responsibility and the role of the provider comes a terror of the weight that such responsibility brings ("escape, attempts to, family, children, from her"; "children, flees from his own"; "delusion, he has neglected his duty"). This terror may reach extreme degrees and lead to his avoiding responsibility and commitment for as long as possible. For a portrait of a man who, in contrast to the responsibility of his work as a surgeon, pursues lightness and flees weight in his personal life with a truly Lycopodium determination, see the character of Tomas in Milan Kundera's novel *The Unbearable Lightness of Being*.

The Lycopodium plant's reliance on air currents to disperse its spores relates to the Lycopodium person's tendencies to inflatedness. His inflated ego constantly needs to bolster itself, polish its image, and surround itself with impressionable admirers; he is plagued by a bloated abdomen and flatulence as a result of inefficient digestion and metabolism.

Each spore of the Lycopodium plant has a hard protective shell composed of fatty acids. Because the spore is so simple, it is virtually indestructible. It can withstand great extremes of temperature and lie dormant for long periods.

The resilience of Lycopodium's spores, combined with the plant's adaptability, are reflected in the Lycopodium person by the quality which Catherine Coulter calls "viability":

Just as the resilient moss conforms to the configuration of the landscape and the changing environment, while proceeding undaunted along its way, Lycopodium's viability ('enormous tenacity for survival': Gutman) stems from his resolute yet conforming nature which permits him to adapt to fluctuating times and circumstances while pursuing his own policies. *

A Lycopodium patient will often present with some breakdown in this viability, often in his digestive system or, more worryingly to him, in his mind.

One-sidedness

In the Lycopodium plant, the branches that grow from the stem favour one side. Development in Lycopodium children and adults is often one-sided, in that they develop their intellectual faculties at the expense of the physical.

Another strong feature in Lycopodium complaints is that they are right-sided or begin on the right and migrate to the left. That right-sidedness is fitting since the right side of the body corresponds to the left side of the brain concerned with logical analytical thoughts. (The left side of the body and the right side of the brain are concerned with imaginative and associative thoughts.) Lycopodium's capacity to live in the rational hemisphere is both their strength and their weakness. Lycopodium is particularly suited to well-developed brains and poor physical capacity. "Strong mind, with weak body" and "Intellectually dominant, yet physically a lily-livered coward" are common in Lycopodium. Bloated abdomen, weak digestive system; even a young adult Lycopodium tends to be pear shaped. The face has many frown lines, especially a V above the bridge of the nose between the eyes—typical of liver conditions. The Lycopodium child is a bookworm, good at his lessons, but may avoid sports and read a book instead. Too physically uncoordinated to shine in physical activity, and too thin and chilly to relish the sports field, he is also too vain to spend time doing anything that would show him up in an adverse light.

---

* Coulter, Catherine R, Portraits of Homeopathic Medicines, Volume I QMP 1998

Lycopodium and the public school ethos

Lycopodiums are often to be found among those children sent to British fee-paying public schools. These children are today being groomed for City jobs, whereas in the past they were being prepared to be posted to countries of the Empire to be rulers there. Typically, a child of a good family would be sent to a preparatory school aged seven and would pine. He would begin his school career at the bottom of the heap, bed-wetting and frightened, acting as fag to a prefect who may introduce him to homosexuality. Later he may move up the hierarchy of prefects, where he will likely do as he has been done to and boss the younger kids around. After he leaves school, that trait is taken out to the colonies, where he bosses around the natives. He will amaze them with the speed of his intellect and take money back home to the mother country. He exercises the power of responsibility for the nation and the Empire. In those days, once they had compensated for their early insecurities, Lycopodiums had a field day. Today you might find them in any business environment, or indeed in most walks of life because of the inherent viability of the Lycopodium personality and also because we put such emphasis on intellectual, left-hemisphere brain activity.

Adolescence

Lycopodium adolescents are often deflated and find their sexual desires thwarted. It is not that they have a particularly strong sexual drive—it is generally normal—but girls don't usually find Lycopodiums attractive, which does not foster their self-confidence or subsequent psychological development. In adulthood too, Lycopodium favours intellectual and sedentary pursuits to such an extent that his vital processes become ever more sluggish.

Insufficient digestive power

A central Lycopodium theme is digestive insufficiency and poor liver function. The word 'liver' reminds us that it is through this organ that we live a full life rather than a restricted one in which our culinary and other desires are thwarted. The digestion reflects the Lycopodium theme of love of power yet feeling of powerlessness, in that his appetite may be great and his hunger canine, yet after a few mouthfuls of food he feels nauseated or bloated. This polarity is also reflected in his sexuality: the desire outruns the performance.

An important factor in Lycopodium's weak digestion is his compromised fat metabolism. Much of the physical pathology is in the liver, the organ which assimilates fats and converts them into glycogen, which in turn provides energy. It is no coincidence that the Lycopodium spore from which the remedy is made contains little but DNA and fatty acids. The Lycopodium person's poor fat metabolism can lead to weight loss, leanness, pain in the liver region, and jaundice. It is also a major factor in Lycopodium's severe loss of physical energy. The glycogen content of the liver drops to its lowest point in the late afternoon hours, which is when Lycopodium feels at his worst. Anywhere between 4-8 in the afternoon may bring an overwhelming incapacity for concentration and performance, when he bites his colleagues' heads off or simply goes off for forty winks.

The Lycopodium person's carbohydrate metabolism is also affected, hence the aggravation from farinaceous, starchy foods. The protein metabolism slows down too, leading to gout and kidney stones. Lycopodium can suffer weakness in the kidneys as much as the liver and there can be a lot of pain with cystitis and urging. Very typical is scanty urination during the day and copious urination at night, hence they can be a bed-wetter. Kidney stones can produce the characteristic red sand-like sediment in the urine.

Lycopodium suffers from a great deal of bloating as the food turns to gas in the stomach and intestines. If the pathology is well advanced the person may develop a duodenal ulcer.

They are very much ameliorated by snacking. They can be hypoglycaemic individuals who need to take frequent high carbohydrate or sugar snacks. Lycopodium persons often keep a bar of chocolate or some sweet snacks in their office drawer to fill the gaps. He gets that 4 o'clock sinking feeling and needs a little snack to keep going to the end of the day. It is in deference to the physiology of this type, and that of Sulphur, that British tea-time in the civil service and many other workplaces is at 11am and 4pm.

They may eat before they go to sleep to assuage the hunger pangs, but will also often get hungry during the night, being at their worst between 3 am and 4 am, when they may get up and snack. They may well wake with indigestion or a bad dream around this time. The typical dream for a Lycopodium person will often have the idea of failure in it.

The Lycopodium person has considerable dependence on others: he fears solitude and desires company, preferring, however, that the other person remains in the next room. This absolves him of the great responsibility of having to entertain the other person; it gives him the illusion of independence, with the ability to avoid commitment.

Lycopodium may learn to live with his failing physical processes, especially as they tend to progress slowly. However, he may be less tolerant of the consequent failure of the mental powers in which he places so much of his sense of self. Indeed, a Lycopodium in poor physical health may complain to his homeopath only of memory lapses or a feeling of encroaching senility.

Lycopodium relies heavily on the power of his speech for his influence over others, and as his mental powers decline, he is dismayed to find that his intellectual and verbal powers begin to become foggy. A brilliant public speaker may lose his memory for words or use the wrong ones. Lycopodium has many rubrics around the use of wrong words, letters or syllables, saying "pears when he means plums".

Sexual insufficiency

Given that the Lycopodium plant is so successful, and that the Lycopodium type is noted for love of power, it is perhaps surprising that both plant and human correlate have a low-key sexual vitality. This is a typically Psoric note. The plant has alternate generations of an asexual, small, sex-cell-producing phase (gametophyte) and a sexual, conspicuous, spore-producing phase (saprophyte). The gametophyte grows slowly and underground, reliant upon a companion fungus for nutrition and taking five or more years to become sexually mature.

When the spores are produced, most remain sterile. The few that germinate take six to seven years to produce leaves, and ten to twenty years to reach full growth—the same time span as a full-grown tree.

In Lycopodium people we also see sexual insufficiency. Phatak mentions "sexual exhaustion; impotence; erections feeble; falls asleep during coition" (reminiscent of the subterranean, slow-growing gametophyte). There are "exhausting pollutions" and "premature seminal emissions". Though these characteristics are predominantly male, there is every reason to suppose that the female equivalents apply in Lycopodium women.

At the opposite polarity, Lycopodiums are prone to phases of lascivious behaviour and libertinism which allow them to enjoy a feeling of sexual power while avoiding commitment. Extra-marital affairs are a prime example, as is the stereotypical boss-and-secretary scenario.

Relating these symptoms back to the large picture, Lycopodium's sexual characteristics fit into the polarity of love of power but sense of powerlessness that lies at the basis of his nature.

The Psoric triad and biblical allegory

Adam and Eve's eating of the apple of the tree of knowledge was the great Psoric sin because it led them to perceive themselves as separate from their creator. This was the birth of questioning: out of this separation flowed doubt and fear, desire and hatred—all the formative ingredients of human suffering. Out of this experience of separation came the yearning to rejoin.

Sulphur, the first remedy in the Psoric triad of Sulphur, Calc carb and Lycopodium, may be used to heal the Psoric disjunction. It strives to rejoin man to the Creator, to connect earth with heaven and male with female. That is why it is the greatest and most fundamental anti-Psoric.

The second remedy of the Psoric triad, Calcarea, is symbolically associated with the sea and moon—with the feminine psyche and union with the mother-protector. Calcarea is concerned with making the home a cradle of safety. Calcarea has the strange delusion that her room is a garden: we are reminded of the lost innocence of the Garden of Eden.

3

33

333333

Lycopodium, the third remedy of the Psoric triad, is about moving out of the home into the world and wondering whether he is up to the task. Lycopodium's emphasis on maintenance and perseverance can be expressed in the notion of man's having to till the soil in order to live. Thrown out of the Garden of Eden where everything is provided for him, he has to work for his living amongst the thistles. While Lycopodium has the rubric "flees from his children", the side of his nature that is often visible is the opposite. He is the one who looks after his children, who upholds the family, and works for their daily bread.

CHAPTER 9

NATRUM MURIATICUM—FLOW
AND CONTAINMENT

A predominantly Psoric remedy

Natrum muriaticum, sodium chloride or table salt, is found in the oceans and in the extra-cellular fluids of animals. In mammals, the foetus develops in salty amniotic fluid. As rock salt, it is mined at the sites of ancient seas, or scraped out of pans in which sea-water has evaporated in the wind and sun.

As we navigate the seascape of Natrum mur, we will naturally evoke images of the ocean. Oceans comprise the larger part of the earth's surface and contain all the land within them. Water seeks its own level; it unites things; it has great depth and cool stillness. 'Oceanic feeling', a term coined by Sigmund Freud, describes feelings of psychic dissolving, as if the small self identity were lost in totality—such as people feel in religious experience, deep love, or when strongly moved by beauty.

All who write about Natrum mur agree that it is adapted to the most sensitive and inwardly vulnerable folk, who require the deepest intimacy in order to thrive. They need to merge, to dissolve, to lose boundaries. But this most desired situation is also their nemesis and deepest fear. Therefore, Natrum mur represents another archetypal anti-Psoric remedy, yet unlike Sulphur, the focus is on the processes of water, or more precisely, on dissolving. The central issue is a dialectic comprising the elements of form and flow, structure/containment and spontaneity.

Water is in constant circulatory movement everywhere on the planet. Warmed by the sun, it evaporates into the atmosphere. When it cools it condenses and forms rain which drains down via small rivulets into the great rivers and estuaries, and finally collects in the ocean. The sun is the first driver of water's movement; the second is the moon's gravitational field, which controls the rhythm of the tides. With this signature in mind, we would expect that Natrum mur would have a relationship to the circulating and flowing water within our bodies—blood, lymph, coryza, tears—and situations such as grief and love disappointments. The remedy also contains the opposite modality of dryness and lack of expressed emotions and tears, buried feelings and isolation.

Lunar and solar modalities

In alchemy, salt represents the feminine principle, while sulphur represents the masculine. In the astrological tradition, elemental water represents feelings—an idea rooted in the ancient civilisations of Mesopotamia and also found in traditional Chinese medicine. The water type is the feeling type. Natrum mur has its strongest root at the emotional level where feelings are deep, still, and unmoving (for example, brooding over past pain), as well as being subject to tidal rhythms and surface storms (such as temper tantrums).

Salt and the beginnings of life

Life on earth began in an aquatic environment, a salty sea. When animals evolved to a point where they could colonise land, it was necessary for each individual cell of the body to surround itself with an environment of salty water. Therefore extra-cellular fluid and the blood are salty, reminiscent of those ancient seas. Amniotic fluid is also salty. The development of the human foetus includes an aquatic phase complete with fish-like gill slits.

Natrum mur is suited to deep and fundamental states and diseases. A major polycrest, it represents an aspect of the nurturing mother archetype and is useful when there has been a deficiency of this aspect of love.

Salt is essential to life and has traditionally been greatly prized. In certain cultures, including desert cultures where perspired salt needs replenishment, salt had a value greater than gold itself. Without salt, one dies. In this context it is understandable that we honour someone by describing them as "the salt of the earth".

Another major use of salt, giving it great commercial value, is the preservation of food. In an age before refrigeration, this was crucial to survival. The concept of preservation by dehydration, which is the mechanism of salt curing, is another pertinent signature of the remedy. Feelings, especially disappointments and griefs, are shrivelled up and dried out, only to be rehydrated in safe solitude.

Another way of working with the signature is to meditate on the story of the circulation of water in relation to the psyche. Imagine a droplet of water at the moment it falls into a lake or the ocean. The droplet has self-identity, but it is also isolated. It is only at the moment of falling into the body of water that it merges and loses its self-ness, and gains a sense of unity and identification with all the other drops. Only then is the sense of isolation lost. For the Natrum mur (and Natrum carb) constitutional type, the question, "Am I me when I am by myself, or do I know me through other people?" is of the essence. Such people are very sensitive on the inside and because they feel everything strongly, and everything is taken within, this becomes the central arena for their suffering. They need to feel that they belong to the ocean rather than being an isolated droplet, but in joining with the ocean of others and the suffering of others, they suffer also.

Babies and children

Natrum mur babies and children can be unbelievably vulnerable. Let us picture the situation of the baby born with a Natrum mur constitution. Arising from close contact with the mother, there is a feeling of complete unity of the psychic auras of baby and mother—the natural state. In tribal Africa, due to the warm climate, nudity is natural; close contact and prolonged breast-feeding is customary. Clothing is not necessary, as it is in the colder, northern climates. Thus in Africa, Natrum mur, though it may be a constitutional remedy for some, rarely develops into pathology. It is not needed very much in countries where the continuum concept of close contact between mother and baby is practised. Neither is it much needed in hot Mediterranean climes, for example, Italy or Greece. It is very much a remedy of British, Irish, Swedish and Russian nationalities, the peoples of the cold Northern countries.

In the early stages of Natrum mur physical pathology, the lips are often affected, with an herpetic eruption or dry crack in the lower lip. Constantine Hering, as a young medical doctor, set out to test the homeopathic hypothesis. He helped himself to globules of potentised Natrum mur until he had advanced the proving so far as to open up a deep crack in his lip. This helped to convince him that homeopathy was up to something! It is with lips that the suckling infant makes its first intimate contact with mother. We re-enact this when we kiss on the lips. A breast-feeding baby develops a small swelling at the centre of the lower lip. Also, there is typically dryness (or profuse and corrosive discharges) of the mucous membranes, such as the vagina. Dryness may be seen as a somatic expression of withdrawal of life energy from those places associated with the maximum amount of most intimate contact.

Picture a baby who suffers repeated disillusionment; this will affect the Natrum mur constitution so deeply that the baby will begin to build up an impenetrable sea wall. The emotionally undernourished baby needs more than the mother can give. When the mother leaves, the baby cries. If the mother doesn't pick her up, it will eventually stop crying, becoming quiet and cut off—a mini-depression.

In the case of the deprived infant, the next stage of development may be total cut-off. The child eventually develops a world of its own.

We may translate these stages into three psychological responses to situations, of which, in Natrum mur, the first two are often found:

- Hysterical responses—shouting for help. Hysterics usually develop psychosomatic symptoms—the symptoms are 'screaming'. Figuratively speaking, they are clutching at a cliff edge with their fingernails.

- Depressive responses. They feel, "Nobody likes me; whatever I do is wrong; however hard I try, it is hopeless. I don't know why I tried in the first place." The basic feeling is not hysterical, but self-critical and withdrawn.

- Schizophrenic responses. Here, the individual has created a complete barrier. "The world is out there but I have no connection to it; I am in my own world. They haven't noticed me at all." Since no one (unless they are enlightened) can face a void, the split-off person, in their own world, populates it with happenings and people. We may observe the genesis of these states in lonely children who invent imaginary playmates. In this world, there might be things that frighten or terrify, or that come as beautiful visions. The paranoid schizophrenic (not a Natrum mur feature) may feel, for example, that people are bugging the telephone or whispering to him from the fireplace. This is an outward projection of the turmoil within.

In all the texts, we see hysteria given as Natrum mur's primary posture, but they may just as readily develop into the second stage of depression.

The protective wall

Because Natrum mur types are vulnerable and sensitive, they progressively build a wall of protection in order to avoid being hurt. For example, when a mother comes to her Natrum mur child to give it the affection it obviously craves, it behaves as if it could not care less. Should this introversion become pronounced, we may eventually observe that well-known feature in Natrum mur children, delayed speech, even as late as four years of age. This is not due to poor brain-power, as in Baryta carb, but to introversion.

They develop willpower in order to keep control of their emotions. The parents may respond by giving less love and Natrum mur will close off even more, and thus receive even less love in return. For example, if something is denied, an apparent promise broken, or something taken away that was expected, this is experienced as a deep hurt. This hurt and tightening inside may be so strong that the child will go into a tantrum. Should the parent try to console the child, the child cries even more. The mother may try to hug the child, and it will fight and punch. The only way to handle this child is to leave it alone, and then it will get rid of its own tantrum when it decides to. The parent will say that they cannot understand the child.

Natrum mur appears to be full of spikes and thorns. Rubrics such as "dwells upon past disagreeable occurrences", "hatred for those who have offended" and "consolation aggravates" give the general idea.

If there is conflict, a Natrum mur type may hysterically rush out of the room, slam the door, rush up to their room, slam the door, throw themselves on the bed and weep into the pillow. Triggers may be little disappointments or emotional slights. Ill effects of mortification, and ailments after grief are the shocks that affect this type of constitution. Silent weeping and silent grieving are often the depressive response.

Adolescence

Adolescence is a time of working out powerful and as yet unconscious emotions. It is common for Natrum mur adolescents to love the arts, especially poetry and music; these evoke such powerful feelings of longing as help them feel emotionally alive, yet in a manner that is absolutely safe. You do not form a personal relationship with a poem; it does not threaten your vulnerable core in a way that a real relationship could.

We expect an adolescent to go to parties, to make many social contacts, to experiment with relationships, and take emotional risks, but this is not so with the Natrum mur type. At a party they sit quietly as Psorics do. Perhaps one or two may gather together, not saying much. They are great observers and will happily watch interactions between people.

Natrum mur is often indicated "after the ill effects of grief." For example, a daughter has formed a very strong relationship with her father, but she has not shown this to anyone. The father dies, and she goes into silent depression. The family had not realised that this relationship was so strong. Natrum mur may form imaginary platonic relationships. If they write romantic poems to an imagined loved one, they may address the envelope, but not send the letter. If they do send it, then they are mortally embarrassed.

There can be hysterical laughing, changing suddenly to hysterical crying, especially after a sudden shock, bad news or bereavement.

Adulthood

Natrum mur types prefer to maintain an objective stance. They become serious, a little Saturnine. They may be wise beyond their years. Other people come to them with their problems, and they are able to give sound advice based upon their observation of what makes others tick. When they are in trouble, however, they turn to no one, as this would mean admitting to their own vulnerability. They care that other people should not be hurt, as they have been often hurt themselves. In speech, they are very careful, to the extent that words may be mulled over before being spoken. They do not want anything they say to be misunderstood.

A Natrum mur man may go off to the pub with friends and get drunk. This will not occur often, as he maintains a close guard on himself. In the morning, he remembers nothing of the previous evening's events, but will ring his friends and apologise for anything offensive he may have said or done.

These are people who listen to others' experiences of life and say, "This is the way of the world". They use other people's experiences to help them build up their reinforced sea-wall. They make good counsellors, priests, lawyers, doctors and therapists. They like to deal with the problems of others, but do not become involved themselves. They remain shielded behind their professional boundary.

Love

The Natrum mur person needs love but is frightened to commit to it in case the love affair goes wrong. Kent writes, "Unrequited affection brings on complaints—she is unable to control her affections and falls in love with a married man". This woman may have been hurt in the past, which proves to her everything she already knew about life, and she says, "This will not happen to me again." She has a tight rein on her emotions, yet the feelings of love and need for a relationship are strong. A relationship with a married man is relatively safe, because she will not tell him of her feelings out of loyalty for his wife; she understands well how his wife would be devastated were he to reciprocate her feelings. Obviously, this is a formula for a repeating cycle of arousal when she meets him, and disappointment when they part. Like Ignatia, Natrum mur is a sterling remedy for hysterical girls and boys in situations of unrequited love.

The Natrum mur type will remember all that has happened, especially the hurtful things. They remember past grief and use the recall of the pain to increase the impenetrability of their sea wall. They will typically remember all the injurious things that have happened in their marriage. It is unlikely that they will break the marriage, as they don't want to harm their partner, so much so that they will not want to mention the things that have wounded them. They chew these things over internally. They put on sad music, which keeps the emotional pot boiling—the music helps to surface the buried feelings. Especially in the adolescent, this may result in profound weeping in private. They think, "Life is cruel, I wish I could die!" but then they think, "If I killed myself that would wound my family irrevocably." Though there may be thoughts of suicide, they are unlikely to go through with it. (Sad music and suicidal thoughts put us in mind of Aurum: this most private perfectionist is a true candidate for self-destruction.)

With adults in a grief situation, the homeopath rarely witnesses uncontrollable crying, except perhaps in bereavement. If they do break down in tears, the crying is terrible to behold. They have built up a shield around themselves, and if a gap suddenly appears, the emotional charge floods out, threatening the integrity of the entire protective structure. They will then try to pull themselves together again before they totally collapse. If they receive consolation, it means that they must give in more, which would threaten an even greater collapse of the self-protecting structure around themselves. This is why "consolation aggravates".

They become closed off, so as to avoid new injuries being inflicted upon them. This is the patient who comes into the consulting room well turned out, with close attention to cleanliness, arriving on time and with their speech worked out precisely. They come in, sit down, look at their watch and say, "How long have we got?" and will proceed to talk about their physical symptoms. They may say, "I have migraines. I'm okay when I wake up, but my head starts around 10 o'clock, it gets worse, and about lunchtime it is so bad I can't eat."

Normally, they have to be prodded into giving emotional information. When they do get to their feelings, they may start to cry; it may be hysterical crying, but is more likely to be restrained, or they may stop themselves and apologise. It is important not to move too near them too soon; they must be given a lot of space. Then trust will build up and they will begin to talk of how they feel. For instance, they often think that others are ungrateful, while they feel that they are considerate of other peoples' feelings. They always send out cards, but get few cards in return. In bitterness, they say to themselves, "This is the way of the world, it's an uncaring place."

They may not be able to express their feelings, even to their loved ones. For example, a man has never been able to say to his wife, "I love you."

This man will keep all his work problems to himself, out of consideration for his family. He will keep sadness to himself. He may be so closed that he evokes reticence in other people. He loves to be near the sea: it uplifts him spiritually, but it makes his symptoms worse. For example, he may have coryza at the seaside, or asthma.

Perfectionism

The protective wall is built stone by stone, piece by piece. These people become fastidious. Words and actions have to be just right. This is not born out of anxiety as it is in the Arsenicum individual who feels that the cosmos is dangerous, that the only way to keep a safe relationship with the chaotic world is by ordering everything. This is precision in the placing and ordering of concepts, emotions and time. They are punctilious. They even walk precisely, with heel first and little springiness in their step. Events must occur at the correct time and in the right order. Natrum mur will say, "I don't like clutter. I like my room to be spartan. I need space." In matters of love, they are perfectionists. They want the perfect relationship, so it is safer to have an imaginary one, for example, with a married man.

From depression, the pathology develops to fears. The main fear is that of claustrophobia. Natrum mur loves space; they cannot bear narrowness. They are so closed off inside, they cannot bear to be closed off outside. They would rather use stairs than lifts. They cannot bear crowds or tolerate crowded shops.

Fixed ideas may develop in terms of what is good and bad. If they apply their fastidiousness to manners, they can become sticklers for correct behaviour.

Hypochondria is another keynote. Natrum mur has a well-stocked medicine cabinet. The main fear is of heart disease. Indeed, arrhythmia is fairly typical. This, combined with fastidiousness, can lead to fear of germs or contagion. She over-washes the floor and surfaces. They often fear robbers—that someone will break through their protective wall and enter their space. A nightmare about a robber will result in a thorough search being conducted. Next day, burglar alarms may be fitted to the house.

While the mental characteristics will be evident, it is likely that physical symptoms will bring a Natrum mur patient to the homeopath in the first instance. These symptoms could range from unspecific weakness, herpetic eruptions (typically of the lips), and sun headaches to serious pathology such as multiple sclerosis or heart disease. They feel everything in the heart, the love centre. Most problems stem from their emotional vulnerability—a truly Psoric note.

Openness

We have the impression of a walled-off and defended person with a vulnerable inner emotional life: water on the inside and stone on the outside. Yet this person, within the boundaries they set themselves, may appear to be open. They almost always permit a video consultation. Often, when the therapeutic 'stage' has become familiar and safe, they can exposes themselves to a degree that may seem truly staggering. They can reveal inner feelings, distress as well as joy, in a manner which is the exact opposite of that which is expected. They often surprise themselves! It is worth recalling that salt is the most water-soluble of all substances. At one pole there is flow, while at the other there is solidity, or as we put it, containment.

Miasms

The character of Natrum mur, with its great inner sensitivity to hurts and slights, and its outward expressions, such as seeking isolation when upset and maintaining distance by becoming overly punctilious are all defining features of the Psoric miasm. The tendency to brood over past troubles, introversion, emotional and physical dryness, and skin affections are also typically Psoric.

CHAPTER 10

SILICA—OBSTINATE YET YIELDING, ELIMINATION OF IMPURITIES
A predominantly Psoric remedy

The homeopathic remedy Silica is made from flint. Flints were formed at the same time as the great limestone deposits were being laid down. At the sea bottom, calcareous skeletons of marine creatures collected—corals, molluscs and the like, along with silica-rich sponges and the microscopic bodies of diatoms, whose cell walls are composed mostly of silica. These compacted over countless millennia. Silica gradually precipitated out of the limestone, accreting unto itself, creating nodules of slowly increasing dimensions—flint stones. These are composed of pure colloidal silicon dioxide. The thrust of flint is to throw out impurities.

Excluding impurities is a feature of crystallisation in general, not just of silica. However, a unique characteristic of flint is being hard yet brittle, fracturing along the angle of impact. For this reason and because flint tools retained a sharp cutting edge, flints were fashioned into cutting tools and weapons by stone-age people. The hardness and resilience of flints also enabled their use as building materials. From this combination of qualities we obtain the Silica traits of 'obstinate yet yielding'.

Joining 'obstinate yet yielding' with the previous characteristic of eliminating impurities, we arrive at the defining signature: Silica types obstinately push out the impurities that got in because they were too yielding. Because they do not have the vital power to complete the task of elimination, they only yield against their will. Potencies of Silica are used to eject splinters in those patients who do not have sufficient power to expel them.

The theme 'obstinate yet yielding' also expresses itself in the Silica rubric "monomania", which implies fixation upon one activity to the exclusion of all others, and "egotism", which implies a fixation of self upon self. The opposite state to egotism is seen in Silica's extreme receptivity to the influence of others—yielding to them—expressed in the rubric, "magnetised, desires to be".

Silicon dioxide in its many forms, for instance, as quartz and as a constituent of granite and feldspar, is the major component of the rocky mantle of our planet. Furthermore, since it is more resistant to erosion than most other materials in the earth's crust, it lends its enduring image to it. For the person needing potentised Silica, form and image are all-important (which could be seen as a form of egotism), as are the refined qualities of integrity and honesty. Refining implies getting rid of unwanted things.

Stamina to eliminate impurities

Conferring stamina enough to eliminate the unwanted and corrupting is Silica's pre-eminent domain. This is the context within which it has gained its reputation of eliminating vaccinal pus. Here it rivals Thuja, the best known of the vaccinosis remedies. A Silica rubric that expresses the alerted state of the immune system to the presence of inimical forces (the aim of vaccination) is "delusion, pursued". The rubric "fixed ideas" expresses the failure of the immune response to revert to its normal resting state after the challenge has disappeared. Thuja, Silica and Mercury all share these rubrics.

As Silica is to maintaining form, Mercurius is to dissolution of form ("criminal", "revolutionary"). It is interesting to note that Silica and Mercury are listed as inimicals. Remedies are termed inimical because they share uncompensated states and sensations which they express in outwardly opposite ways. Both Silica and Mercurius give the strength to throw out infection, the former representing brittle hardness, the latter liquefaction and decay—for, as we have seen, Mercury is the amalgamating metal.

Structure and order

Compounds of silicon dioxide enter into everyday life as:

- quartz chips, used in the most accurate clock mechanisms and in modern transmitters to regulate oscillations—in the case of precision clocks, to within a second in thousands of years ("fastidious"; "conscientious about trifles"; "self-control");

- semiconductors made of aluminium silicate and used by the computer industry. The area of California where computer industries proliferate is called Silicon Valley.

With reference to computers, the "delusion, left side does not belong to him" is a Silica single remedy rubric. The implication is that only the right side exists. The right side of the body corresponds to the left side of the brain, concerned primarily with logical, analytical thoughts. Silica suits the left-brained individual, dominated by processes of reason, interested in structure and order. A good example of this mindset is afforded by systems analysts and computer programmers. Had Kent lived in the computer age, he surely would have included these professions in his Lectures when he wrote:

> *Silica is ... for such brain-fag as belongs to professional men, students, lawyers, clergymen. A lawyer says, "I have never been myself since that John Doe case." He went through a prolonged effort and sleepless nights followed.*

The obstinate yet yielding Silica type

With flint being hard and inflexible (obstinate) yet easily fissured (yielding), so we may find the Silica type feeling vulnerable and overcome with forebodings of failure, fearing that nothing will succeed. Vital power gives out. We picture him as spineless, chilly, and prematurely balding. He may lose heart for the lustful life, perhaps retreating into literature—a safer world of predictable structures and fantasies where he is not challenged by confrontations with reality. The strength of the medicine made of pure flint is his doctor! The Silica personality is refined, just as, by a gradual (Psoric) process, the forming flintstone rejects all impurities, and refines itself.

If Silica's fixity is challenged, he can show irritability ("irritable and irascible when aroused"—Kent). Flint-lock pistols and rifles used fragments of flint to ignite gunpowder, as they spark when struck.

Image and form

Silica types refine an image of themselves, which is played out in the profession they enter. They choose a career where rigid adherence to the form is the important thing. They might be a lawyer, preacher or religious person, an architect or anything else where a fixed structure exists and they can work and excel within it. They will say, "I am a such-and-such", and define themselves that way—anything not to be yielding.

The yielding type of Silica child can be timid and bashful at school. We recall the typical Silica constipation, the "bashful stool", which slides out a little way and then shies back in again. The energy to push out the stool runs out before the impurity can be expelled. In order to compensate for their inward lack of form, these types thrive on order and routine and often become fixed on one way of doing a thing ("monomania"). The term 'anal retentive' suits this type. The fixations of Silica children can be extreme and may be reminiscent of the mindless repetitive behaviour seen in some mentally retarded people. Physically, too, they can be backward in a way similar to Calcarea: they can have rickety legs and are prone to a dome-shaped abdomen well beyond the usual years—natural in a toddler but not in a 3- or 4-year-old.

In general, Silica children are not particularly affectionate. We could say that they relate to masculine modes of operating rather than feminine. There is noted clinical evidence of Silica babies being intolerant to their mother's milk. Speaking psychologically, we could say that they cannot respond to the flow of the feminine, being rooted in the fixity of the masculine.

Silica types get very confused if not given clear boundaries. Conversation can confuse and aggravate them unless it is clearly ordered, such as that which a lawyer or doctor has with a client.

They tend to be chilly people because of the lack of vital response. They must have heat around them and are exquisitely sensitive to cold and drafts, yet they perspire easily, especially on their hands, feet and head. The Silica handshake, like that of Calcarea, is famed for its 'wet fish' clamminess and lack of fibre.

Physical symptoms

Silica children can be superficially confused with Calcarea, since they are also rather slow to move out into the world. But whilst Calcarea types are flabby and fleshy (minus quality and plus quantity), Silica children have a fineness about them. They are usually thin and refined. Their hair may be fine and their skin delicate. Their bitten nails, often to the quick, expose their timidity. Toenails are likely to be ingrowing, to split easily, or to be fungus-infected. All nails may have white spots. Hair loss and balding are common under stress, even in children. Recurrent infections and suppurations are typical.

Silica is of benefit in chronic sick headaches. The pain rises from the base of the brain to the top of the head and settles over one of the eyes, usually the right. The pain is sticking, tearing and pressing in character. It is much worse by motion, noise, or light.

It is often true of Silica that the body parts that should be hard or resilient are too soft (weak hair and nails) whereas the parts that should be soft are too hard (keloid scars, corns, hard boils in soft tissues, and indurated slow-to-heal suppurating wounds).

Miasms

Miasmatically Silica expresses Psora to a 'T', with its monomaniacal adherence to traditional structures and forms—dotting its i's and crossing its t's.

Flints were formed at the time when the great limestone deposits were being laid down. Like Calcarea, Silica refers to the foundations of life's processes and to weakness and diseases of bones, nails and teeth, as well as infantile malnutrition and problems of breast-feeding. Later, this weak foundation in life expresses as the typically Psoric reluctance to venture forth. As one patient expressed it, "I feel that I have a predisposition to fail. It is as if a shadow stretches before me over which I stumble and fall." Flint is hard and inflexible (obstinate) yet easily fissured (yielding). This pair of opposing tendencies expresses the Psoric miasm beautifully. Silica is similar to Lycopodium, with its polar opposites of love of power and cowardice, in that losing face lies at the root of both remedies. Loss of strength, confidence, and the power to sustain effort are Psoric hallmarks.

CHAPTER 11

RHUS TOX—FREEZING UP

A Psoro-Sycotic remedy
(also representing Tubercular and AIDS miasms)

Rhus tox is the remedy made from poison ivy, a plant which abounds mainly on the East Coast of North America. The ill effects in someone who has been in contact with poison ivy include primarily, skin lesions; secondarily, respiratory and digestive symptoms; and finally, joint pathology. In the treatment of chicken pox, Rhus tox is a first-line remedy. Those sensitive to poison ivy develop persistent itching blisters. They may also develop rheumatic pains. Clarke's Materia Medica states:

> *Those who care for signatures will not fail to connect the cardinal aggravations of Rhus tox—at night and from damp— with the increased virulence of the plant at night and in damp atmospheres.*

At night, mists gather in the thickets and low ground where poison ivy grows. Damp conditions predominate. Worse for damp and worse in the shade and cold are the primary modalities of Rhus tox. At the physical level of manifestation, the Rhus tox theme may be expressed as: tends to freeze up and is better for warmth and continued movement.

The patient for whom Rhus tox is the simillimum must have a preponderance of cold and damp qualities within, in order that the outward accentuation of these qualities should lead to disease. In terms of the physical body, the coolest and wettest disease phenomena would be herpetic vesicular eruptions and diseased synovial capsules, primary seats of Rhus tox pathology. (As a point of comparison, the hottest and wettest place would be arterial blood in the large vessels; a remedy epitomising an imbalance of this nature might be found in Glonoinum. The hottest and driest would be an inflamed surface; a remedy epitomising this imbalance might be found in Belladonna.)

In Rhus tox pathology, affected joints are ameliorated by warm applications and continued movement. Initial movement that breaks the ice, so to speak, is painful, but continued movement is warmth-producing, like friction, and ameliorates.

Suspicion

These physical processes have a mental corollary: suspicion, secretiveness and wariness are characteristic. This may be understood as a freezing up at an emotional level. Rhus tox bold type rubrics include fears at night, when the temperature drops and when people cannot be seen because of the darkness; fear of people; timidity at night; and dwelling on past disagreeable occurrences, or becoming emotionally mired, after midnight. Warmth is manifest on emotional as well as physical levels. Thus freezing up—a preponderance of cold water within—finds its emotional expression in such symptoms as lack of trust (not flowing) and delusions of being poisoned, pursued, watched and murdered.

As an example of a Rhus tox psychotic episode, we may cite the case of a policeman—an appropriate activity for a suspicious person—who has lost his job because he has been caught committing a theft. He had previously run for fitness, but after he was sacked, running became an obsession. The more he ran, the better he felt. Yet eventually he had to stop! His sleep was crowded by dreams of superhuman exertion and running over fields being chased by enemies. He would awaken with further impulses to escape. Yet initial movement aggravated. He suspected that he was paranoid; he felt stiff and stuck.

Rhus tox grows in great groups of its own kind with few other species intermingled, along river valleys, exuding its poisonous miasma. Just as the plant grows in family groups, so the Rhus tox emphasis is on the family (or in the case of the policeman, the neighbourhood) and providing for their safety. The message is that outsiders should keep out. This image reinforces the uncompensated Rhus tox characteristics of suspicion and lack of trust, alongside the typical sensation of stiffness and being held tight.

This note is reflected in an odd feature of skin rashes caused by contact with poison ivy: they are 'contagious', in that if the rash is allowed to come into contact with unaffected skin, that skin may also 'catch' the rash. The rash can also be passed to another person through contact. Thus a person with a poison ivy rash has to keep the affected part isolated from other parts of his body and from other people. No contact is allowed. Small wonder then, that such a person may feel dirty and excluded, may feel as if they have to run away, although expressing the opposite traits of trustworthiness and stiffness.

In summary, the psychological state of the Rhus tox patient is characterised by 'freezing up', as expressed by the modality "worse for cold and initial movement". However, once the ice has been broken, such a person is naturally inclined to continue established emotional attachments. We find that Rhus tox patients are usually family-oriented and exhibit loyalty and trustworthiness. They are likely to be stalwart citizens, upholding traditional values in a manner reminiscent of Calcarea. Indeed, Calcarea is the chronic of Rhus tox.

Miasms

From a miasmatic perspective, Psora is represented by anxiety for the family, freezing up in cold conditions, and the itch vesicle. Sycosis is represented by feeling worse for damp and the suspicious and secretive manner.

There is also a relationship to Tubercular and AIDS miasms. Tubercular traits (see Chapter 17) include the marked relief from continued movement and the theme of the family. Tuberculinum has been uprooted from family and homeland, whereas Rhus tox needs to protect the family.

AIDS miasm traits (see Chapter 19) include feelings of dirtiness inside and lack of trust outside, with communication of the message that outsiders should keep out. Physical symptoms of cold and flu, blisters and vesicles may correlate with this mental state.

All who live with Rhus tox plants in their vicinity treat the entire area with respect and teach their children to do likewise. This note of keeping clear of contagious and dangerous influences reminds us of the AIDS miasm. In end-stage pathology of AIDS/'Slim' disease, involving severe thrush and debilitating diarrhoea, Rhus tox is a remedy to bear in mind.

CHAPTER 12

THUJA—TREE OF LIFE AND DEATH

A Sycotic and AIDS miasm remedy

In recent homeopathic Materia Medicas, a well-developed yet one-sided portrait of Thuja has emerged. This one-sidedness may be inherent in Thuja's picture, with its marked symptoms of a divided self, but in this chapter we shall attempt to paint in some of the neglected areas.

Thuja, though familiar to all homeopaths, is often missed because we have a preconception of how a Thuja patient ought to present. Likewise, we may have a preconception of how Carcinosin ought to present: say, sympathetic, suppressed and dutiful; or how Causticum ought to present: sympathetic yet tough, a fighter for causes. With Thuja as with Natrum mur, once the therapeutic 'stage' has become familiar and safe, even these closed patients open to a degree which may seem truly staggering. They can reveal inner feelings in a way which is the exact opposite of what is stereotypically expected.

Stereotypical pictures are useful hooks upon which to hang information. However, when it comes to practice, it is often best to throw them away. For there are almost as many variations on the theme of the basic pictures as there are people. It is of greater service and safer to think in terms of processes and themes, for in this manner, the uncompensated state can be uncovered.

What, then, are Thuja's themes, what process is occurring in the soul and body of the Thuja patient?

The remedy

The remedy is prepared from a tincture of the fresh green twigs of Arbor vitae, the Western red cedar, known as the Tree of Life. Referring to Biblical allegory, we are reminded of the tree of eternal life, the fruits of which the expelled Adam and Eve did not eat. Had they done so, they would have become immortal. Disease and death would never have assailed them.

The growth habits of Arbor vitae illustrate the dichotomy of life and death which runs through the remedy Thuja. This is a famed evergreen ornamental tree, commonly used as hedging because of its abundant and close-knit growth. As a mature tree, it naturally develops a clipped appearance and a neat conical shape. The necessity of maintaining this perfect image (a characteristic Thuja concern) is crucial with Arbor vitae, because only those parts of the tree that are exposed to the sun stay green and alive-looking. All the parts beneath the surface that are hidden from the sun quickly turn brown, dry and seemingly dead. A foray into the hollow space framed by the tree's outer canopy convinces you that you are in the world of the dead.

From this signature and the proving symptoms, we can derive an appreciation of the central process of the remedy Thuja: the perceived need to hide one's darkness within, one's sin, to cover it up beneath a glossy and presentable exterior. Miasmatically, Thuja is predominantly anti-Sycotic. Inside there are feelings of guilt; outside there is gloss and exuberant growth. The AIDS miasm also comes in with respect to the themes of death and fragility of the body.

Life and death

Where is the seat of life in the physical body? The Japanese and Chinese would indicate the Hara, the umbilical region. Thuja is the only remedy in the Materia Medica to have the symptom "delusion, animals are in the abdomen", and it is italicised, which indicates that several provers experienced it. There are also delusions that "voices are in his abdomen" and that "she thought herself pregnant." Thuja's false pregnancy lacks the hysterical and rapidly alternating states of Crocus. It is rather a fixed notion that it is so, complete with movements as of foetal limbs and swelling of abdomen.

These are symptoms of a superabundance of vegetative/animal life, as are the fleshy warts for which Thuja is famed. The symptom "hairiness in unusual places" also expresses the over-abundant life principle. Hering writes of Thuja:

There is a surplus of producing life; nearly unlimited proliferation of pathological vegetations, condylomata, warty sycotic excrescences, spongy tumours, and spongy pock exudates [which] organise hastily; all morbid manifestations are excessive, but appear quietly, so that the beginning of the diseased state is scarcely known.

In the opposite modality, we have the delusions that the "body is brittle"; that the "body is delicate", "diminished" and "too thin"; that the body is "made of glass"; and "in insanity, will not be touched". These symptoms give the impression of innate fragility, as if there were a deficiency of life.

From a psychological view, we might question why these erroneous fixations about the state of the body arise? What does it mean that the brittle and glass-like body has an animal in the Hara? One possibility would be that Thuja's process is on a continuum between a super-abundance of animal energy on the one hand, an extreme weakness and transparency of life on the other, and a body hardly able to house and sustain the inner being. This finds its psychical analogue in states such as "desires death" and "loathing of life".

It has been suggested that Thuja should be considered in cases of the ill effects of HRT, where animal oestrogen is introduced into the blood. Premarin, the best known HRT preparation, is refined from the urine of pregnant mares. The underlying fear which motivates many women to take HRT is brittle bone syndrome, recalling Thuja's sense of brittleness.

By way of extending the range of this life-death dynamic, we may cite the delusion that she is under superhuman control—the superhuman controlling the lower human, or the higher aspects of the self controlling the animal being. Thuja patients are prone to massive guilt complexes, as evidenced by rubrics alluding to doing wrong, being a criminal and reproaching himself. The superhuman aspect of the divided self sits in judgement on the animal aspect.

Secretiveness

If the eyes are the windows of the soul, Thuja's windows are shuttered. Thuja is bold type alongside Opium in the rubric, "contracted pupils", which is enlightening, given the themes of shame and deceit that both remedies share. This interpretation sits well with Vithoulkas' description of Thuja's guarded, hidden personality, who, walled off behind a lifetime's habit of secretiveness, is viewed by others as manipulative and sneaky. Thuja is one of very few remedies to have skin eruptions only on those parts of the body which are covered by clothes, bringing to mind the theme of a shameful secret.

Clarke, quoting Millspaugh, writes, "The Arbor vitae assumes a conical form with such true lines as to appear 'clipped', thus forming one of our most valued high-hedge trees". Hedges are grown to provide a screen. Douglas Borland suggests that Thuja patients are well-mannered, sensitive, polite, truthful and scrupulous in all their undertakings. My experience tends to favour this latter description, perhaps because it is the one modelled upon a more traditional British temperament. Yet both stereotypes are built upon a pathological need for correctness.

Thuja patients, who tend to be over-cautious, over-civilised and over-conscientious, are not noted for outbursts of rage or violence. However, Thuja appears in an interesting sub-rubric of anger: "violent anger when things do not go after his will". This is a typically fixed idea, that things should go "after his will", and is a pronounced choleric symptom. We also find "anger from contradiction", "easy anger", "anger at trifles", "beside oneself" and "being beside oneself from trifles". Why trifles? Because this conforms to the choleric ideal of conformity and order, of everything belonging in its precise place. Such individuals build the structures of civilisation, laws and social mores in order to hold at bay the advancing tide of fears and chaos, and in Thuja's case, the tide of the instinctual and animal.

Division

The Sycotic state manifests as an idea or obsession that is fixed, as a fig-wart is fixed to a muco-cutaneous border. Religious fanaticism and fixed religious ideas are a Thuja stronghold, erected from an excessively rigid sense of correctness. Thuja is listed in bold type in the rubric "conscientious about trifles", and is found under "fastidious". On one side of the divide is correct, orderly, right, on the other is wrong. The more

Thuja pulls right and wrong to the extreme positions, the more division he feels and the greater is his sense of not belonging, even isolation.

This state is a little different from the Anacardium split of good angel versus bad devil, although many rubrics overlap, including the sense of separateness. However, this is far more pronounced in the Anacardium patient, who may be unfeeling and cruel, and can lack all moral scruples. Anacardium is a species of cashew nut, the sweetest of nuts, the kernel of which is protected by the corrosive skin from which the remedy is prepared. Likewise, Anacardium patients can be sweet (the stereotypical image of the cruel, cursing maniac may be absent) and we may find a striving spiritual follower of the doctrine of love and peace. Both Thuja and Anacardium may be found in religious brotherhoods. Hell-raising Anacardium and preaching-and-converting Thuja are to be seen in the spiritual market place!

With Thuja, the division is one of moral sense versus animal instincts. A Thuja patient may appear to be a fascist moralist who doesn't trust instincts and would put them under lock and key. If Thuja patients feel this way, they certainly don't want other people to see into them. They may feel dirty, like shit, unlovable, unworthy. A patient who was prescribed Thuja 10M described a dream the following night (a new and probably a proving symptom) in which she visited the home of friends and was invited to eat her own shit recycled into sausages. Indeed, if we couple this state of mind with the expression of being made of glass, which is transparent as well as brittle, then it is easy to comprehend Thuja's fear of strangers and reluctance to open up in a spontaneous manner. These characteristics are representative of the Syphilitic and AIDS miasms.

Thuja is divided in respect of left- and right-hand sides of the body, with a marked aggravation on the left side. It is customary to vaccinate on the left-hand side. Symbolically, the left side represents the unconscious and all processes tending towards death, dissolution of structure and anarchy, while the right side represents organised structure and the function of reason.

It is interesting to note the relationship between Thuja and Silica. Both remedies are divided, fixed and fastidious; both feel that they have done wrong and are pursued by the projections of their guilty conscience; both are major remedies for the ill effects of vaccination. Yet Silica has the delusion that the left side does not belong, in that the right side is all that there is. Just as Silica dominates the right side, so Thuja dominates the left. As Silica is to dominance of form, so Thuja is to dissolution of form (and anarchic growth and proliferation). Yet both remedies keep up appearances, Silica because the element's nature is to give shape and definition, and Thuja because shape and definition are threatened by the process of undefined proliferation.

The process of death

A singular symptom of Thuja is the delusion that he is "divided in two parts and could not tell of which part he had possession on waking". Why? Perhaps because he could not successfully or completely return to his delicate, brittle body after sleep. We may picture sleep as a detachment of the physical being from the psychic, and awakening as their reunion. Rubrics expressing Thuja's failure to achieve this reunion include: "delusion, mind and body separate"; "fancies body was too small for soul, or that it was separated from soul"; "body is lighter than air"; "being divided into two parts"; "being double." Another way of picturing this is as a division between light and heavy elements. When we die, the light, ascending elements separate off from the heavy, earth-bound elements of the corpse.

Thuja individuals are suffering from an excess of vegetative life, as indicated by the delusion of an animal in the abdomen and the tendency to neoplasms. The typical condylomata are pedunculated and reminiscent of a broccoli flower bud or an umbilical cord and foetus. These manifestations represent one pole of the continuum of life (the Arbor vitae), while the other pole is represented by death. There are many symptoms around death: "conviction of death"; "desires death"; "thought he was about to die"; "the time had come to die"; "sees dead persons"; "dreams of the dead, of dead bodies, of dying".

In the Generalities section of the Repertory we find Thuja's times of aggravation to be in the evening, at night, and at 3 am and 3 pm. The occurrence of polar opposite states, in this case, time modalities, confirms the relative importance of the modality. Most deaths and births occur between 3 and 4 am. This time has been called the hour of the wolf, and those required to watch at night call this time "the dog watch hour". This is the time of the coming in and the going out of the soul, of the lowest metabolic rate, of nightmares, ghosts and the first breath of the newborn.

Thuja has dreams of falling, and falling from a high place. Falling dreams often express an anxiety about physical death, and are suggestive of the soul's re-entry into the body after a period of deep sleep. Also, falling dreams may express residual memories of incarnation, where the soul enters the body it is to occupy for a lifetime. It is not accidental that the rubric "abortion in the third month" contains Thuja. It is during the third month of pregnancy that the foetus's sex is manifest and that human features develop. Before this time, it is not possible to distinguish between animal and human foetuses. Abortion at this critical moment indicates a major hitch in the transition from animal into human form. The delusion "fancies body was too small for soul" expresses this idea beautifully.

These and the following Delusion symptoms give us an idea of the major dynamic at work in Thuja: "body lighter than air, floating in air", that "he is ethereal", "incorporeal" and "light". If the body were lighter than air, then it would rise up. Were it to rise up, lighter than air, then it would not be a body, it would be a spirit or soul—unanchored, as befits its state in the period before conception, during the initial phases of gestation, and after death. As well as representing an ungrounded state, these symptoms represent a state of physical fragility, of thinness. Boericke, Clarke and Kent all write about thin, emaciated Thuja patients.

When the homeopath Jeremy Sherr talked about Thuja, he suggested that such patients were stuck between life and death, between the end of one cycle and the beginning of the next. One might say they are in the transitional place occupied by the soul just before the third month of pregnancy or just after bodily life ends. This sheds light on Thuja's delusion of the body and soul being separate (though not yet completely separated), and on the delusion of not knowing which part of themselves they inhabit upon awakening.

Vaccinosis

Compton Burnett has written eloquently and convincingly of vaccinosis and its various manifestations. In his book Delicate, Backward, Puny and Stunted Children, he makes a clinically well-documented case for the use of Thuja in vaccine-damaged patients. Others who may benefit hugely from Thuja are ME patients, emaciated patients with extreme weakness, stunted children of parents who are Sycotic, children who have been vaccinated, and those with parents who have been vaccinated.

Vaccines could be said to be foreign disease proteins introduced into the blood. Not only are these proteins animals in themselves, in that they are micro-organisms, but vaccines are grown in animal tissues—often a series of tissues from different animals such as cows, pigs and hamsters in a process called "attenuation". This process is meant to weaken the vaccine micro-organisms to the point that they will not cause the disease against which they will confer immunity.

The immune system reacts to a foreign protein in the blood by fighting it with fever and then remembering the protein's structure (its key signature) for future more effective defence responses. This necessarily ties up the defence system's memory into a fixed state of readiness. Thuja has a monomania about being pursued, to use Repertory language. It is wonderful and terrifying to speculate upon the widespread genesis of the Thuja state, planted by vaccination into the already Sycotic soil of the population.

Confusion

One of Thuja's characteristic symptoms is confusion of mind. This state expresses in a number of ways. For instance, patients may say that they lose their way in well-known streets. They may become confused while talking, as well as walking. They lose words, phrases and even complete sentences. The same phenomenon may occur when they are writing: listed in bold type is the rubric, "mistakes in writing." They use wrong words, or forget what they wanted to say at the point of saying it or writing it. Words, phrases and sentences may slip into a memory hole, a little memory death. This is reminiscent of Medorrhinum, which is a close analogue. As Medorrhinum is to the state that arises with gonorrhoea, so Thuja is to the state which arises when the Sycotic taint has been passed through generations and has developed into a more passive way of being. It has become civilised and introverted.

Water

In common with most other Sycotic remedies, Thuja is applicable to hydrogenoid (worse for water) constitutions. Clarke's Materia Medica tells us that Thuja

> *abounds in the upper zones of North America, from Pennsylvania northwards, where it often forms what are commonly known as cedar-swamps. It grows upon the rocky banks of rivers, and in low, swampy spots.*

Thuja provings brought out a general aggravation from cold and wet conditions. Sycosis tends to overproduce fluids, including catarrh. Such patients have too much water within, and so are ameliorated in dry climates and very much worse for wet conditions. Rheumatism and asthma are especially aggravated. There is a great affinity for joints and capsules. Thuja and Medorrhinum are important asthma remedies and often clear up the chronic state behind frequent Arsenicum acutes. Thuja and Arsenicum both have presentiments of death, both have fixed ideas, both feel that they are being observed, and both feel contaminated—by disease in Arsenicum's case, and by animal poisons in the case of Thuja.

Miasms

Just as Sulphur is to Psora and Mercurius is to Syphilis, so Thuja is to Sycosis: it is said to be its defining remedy. The most distinctive Sycotic mental/emotional trait is the often hidden inner nature. Thuja patients may feel that they are ugly, disgusting, and unlovable. This is the result of the original, uncompensated state of separation of soul from body and resultant proliferation of growths—warts and the like—that in turn leads to a Thuja patients' sense of ugliness. They are renowned for feeling guilty; a person who has lost connection with her soul may ask herself who else has got into her body. It is as if she has done something unspeakably wrong. The ultimate cover-up is the compensated state, the secretive shield.

Thuja shares with the AIDS miasm feelings of ugliness, unworthiness and secretiveness. The primary concept of the AIDS miasm is a breaching of a boundary. In Thuja this becomes the boundary of the body, which is tenuous, fragile and brittle. Death occurs when this boundary fails and the soul floats free ("delusions, body lighter than air"; "delusions, floating in air").

Thuja's time-honoured relationship with vaccine-damaged individuals speaks eloquently of its belonging to the AIDS miasm. In such cases, the boundary of the immune system has been breached. In cases of Gulf War syndrome, soldiers were given multiple and often experimental vaccines. They subsequently became unable to function because all manner of diseases assailed them, including conditions similar to myalgic encephalomyelitis (ME).

CHAPTER 13

PULSATILLA—NEED FOR SUPPORT

A Psoro-Sycotic remedy

The common names for the Pulsatilla plant are windflower, shame-faced maiden, or Pasque (Easter) Flower. A member of the anemone family, it has a beautiful purple flower that hangs down like the head of a shame-faced maiden. Its soft structure and pendulous habit means that it can be much affected by the wind blowing on it. The homeopathic Pulsatilla type is emotionally changeable and is much better from open air. They wilt indoors, in a centrally heated room with the windows shut, although they are often chilly people. Pulsatillas grow in groups, as if needing the protection of their fellows. They favour habitats with trees or rocks nearby to protect them from frost, as they flower early, ahead of competitors.

Similarly, the Pulsatilla type needs the support of stronger friends or family to look up to and lean on. They droop in competitive, hard environments. They like water yet need a well-drained sandy soil, reflected in the homeopathic Pulsatilla type's thirstlessless during fever and tendency to ailments from getting the feet wet.

The underlying concept of Pulsatilla is fluidity, changeability, softness and forsaken feeling ("clinging, of children to mother"). Pulsatilla types are affectionate, timid, emotional, mild and weepy. The name Pasque Flower reminds us that the Pulsatilla plant flowers at Easter, which in the Northern Hemisphere falls in the changeable month of April. They are changeable, with alternating moods ("laughing or weeping tendency, on all occasions") and they easily feel left out ("delusions, of emptiness"; "delusions, always alone").

Emotional sponge

Pulsatillas are worse for frost, both physical and emotional. They want to please, are very sympathetic and like to receive a lot of affection ("kisses, caressing and kissing"; "affectionate, children").

They can be described as an emotional sponge, in that they take in more than they give back ("selfishness"). A relationship with a Pulsatilla is unequal ("avarice, wants all for himself"). You can feel drained by them. The mothers of Pulsatilla children can become Sepia-like because they are over-stretched by the constant onslaught of demands. Attention is the soul-food of the Pulsatilla type. To be deprived of it enhances the uncompensated feeling of raw vulnerability and makes them more likely to progress to habits of weeping or charming attention-stealing, or to develop a talent for emotional bargaining.

Pulsatilla children and adults are better for consolation and for being listened to and consoled. They also have many fears. The strongest fear is of being alone. They easily feel left out, isolated and forsaken. They may also have claustrophobia, fear of darkness, fear of the things that might come out of the dark and frighten them, fear of animals and fear of sex. There can be a fear of insanity, though you see this in adults, not in children. The following Mind rubrics cast light upon the madness that Pulsatilla types can develop: "aversion, to opposite sex"; "delusions, naked man in bed"; "delusions, surrounded by strangers" (an expression of needing one trusted friend while being terrified of outsiders); "despair, religious"; "constant prayer"; "dementia, old people, in, with foolish talking".

Water

Pulsatillas are thirstless. They don't drink much, and even during a fever, they have to be reminded to take fluids. Similarly, Pulsatilla plants thrive in a well-drained sandy soil; they can't bear water-logging. Emotionally, they overflow with feelings and tears—they cannot abide even more water. This is seen whenever several Pulsatilla types crop up within one family, for they cannot cope well with the competition of another's attention-seeking tears. Acute jealousy can arise and is not expressed in a mild and watery manner; it can be fierce. However, Pulsatilla's innate changeability ensures it is short-lived.

They tend to have digestive problems, with a strong aversion to fatty foods and dairy, particularly cream and cheese. Eating party-type foods would have very bad effects, making them feel ill, with vomiting and nausea. Pulsatilla is a favoured acute remedy for a child suffering in this way after a party.

The stereotype Pulsatilla is blonde and blue-eyed with a fair complexion and of a mild and yielding disposition. This should not exclude black people, who can just as easily need Pulsatilla as pink folk. Pulsatillas flush up at the slightest emotion. Menopausal flushing can also respond well to the remedy.

In children, there is a tendency to earaches. Pulsatilla produces a lot of bland discharges. These can take the form of colds that turn into green or yellow-green discharges from the nose. The discharge can also block up the Eustachian tubes, causing deafness with much pain in the ears. This is a typical Sycotic note in a predominantly Psoric remedy.

It is an important remedy for mumps, though due to vaccinations the disease is not often seen today. For mumps that metastasise (when other glands swell, especially testes in boys and breasts in girls), Pulsatilla can work wonders in bringing the swelling down, stopping pain and preventing subsequent infertility. This is also a Sycotic note.

Pulsatilla children often sleep on their back with their hands right up above their head in a wide-open position. The time of night when they are supposed to be going to sleep is often a bad time for Pulsatilla children, since they suffer when on their own. They like to have company to assuage their fears as they go to sleep. The best scenario would be a shared bedroom with parents and other siblings. Pulsatilla's dependency upon others is so great that it usually modifies jealousy and hides it, turning potential enmity into a co-operative venture. Covering up and hiding is another Sycotic tendency.

Sweetness

Pulsatilla children are sweet, almost effeminate, and needy. They obviously feel jealous when another is getting more attention than them. But alongside the jealousy, there is a yielding which later transforms into being in league with the sibling. It is most unusual for a Pulsatilla child to be defiant and act out the jealousy except in an acute emotional crisis. This is the opposite of the passionate Lachesis type described in the next chapter.

It is usual for adolescent Pulsatilla types to suffer love disappointments. Then they feel cut to the quick because this undermines their weak sense of independence ("grief, silent, with submissiveness"). The adolescent Pulsatilla can lay claim to a calm part of their mind by phasing out the rest of the world ("delusions, surroundings do not exist"). They may choose to retreat into soft music or romantic novels ("desires literature").

In childbirth, Pulsatilla has won its laurels as the remedy for foetal malpositions. It certainly works wonders for Pulsatilla ladies who are like an April day, sunny one moment and weepy the next. If they also cling to sympathy and cuddles, while needing frequent reassurance, then the diagnosis is all but clinched.

Monomania

As an antidote to too much submissiveness, to too great a tendency to yield under emotional pressure, Pulsatilla types can develop a particular species of monomania. It can begin innocently enough with "desires, numerous, various things, refused when offered", and progress to "conscientious, about trifles, pedant, too much". Their progressed monomania usually expresses in relation to food, religion and sex. They can be fanatical about diets, food faddists who believe that certain items of food will harm them.

As for sex, flirtatious Pulsatilla types can have a field day: "amorous"; "lascivious"; "nymphomania". Yet just as commonly they can turn away from it: "aversion, to women, looks upon them as evil beings and is afraid their presence is injurious to his soul".

Pulsatilla is prone to religious monomania: "delusion, has visions, strikes at them and holds up the cross"; "religious affections, fanaticism". Naturally, religious fanaticism translates into modern equivalents and may be political, with fascist and communist governments providing impressive models and structures within which Pulsatilla types may abide and feel safe. Fundamentalism underpins sects and movements such as homeopathic groups who follow certain gurus. This clinging in a Pulsatilla type is an extreme compensation for the uncompensated, now lonely, now fulfilled, state of emotional changeability.

Miasms

In miasmatic terms, Pulsatilla's primary insecurity—their need for connection with another—is an expression of Psora, while their emotional and physical changeability is an expression of Sycosis.

CHAPTER 14

LACHESIS—BURSTING OUT OF RESTRICTION
A Syphilo-Sycotic remedy

Lachesis derives from the venom of the Bushmaster or Surukuku snake of the Brazilian rainforests. It is ferocious and much feared by the natives, for its venom is both neurotoxic (affects the nervous system) and haemolytic (inactivates blood clotting).

There is a famous story about Constantine Hering's inadvertent proving of Lachesis. In this account, while Hering and his wife were zoologising in the Brazilian rainforest, a native presented the doctor with a live Bushmaster snake in a wicker cage. When the villagers heard of this, they fled their huts, leaving Hering to express venom into a bottle unassisted. Hering, affected by the snake poison, passed into a coma. Upon recovery, it is reported that he asked his wife: "What did I do? What did I say?"

However, according to Greg Bedayn*, Hering never went to Brazil and the Surukuku venom came from a captive snake.

Our point in recounting the aggrandised story and Bedayn's debunking of it is to highlight two aspects of Lachesis pathology: first, that of excessive ego, boasting, lies and deceit for self-aggrandisement; and second, debunking, which cuts us down to size, and renders us unimportant and ineffective.

What is certain is that a formal proving was conducted by Kent and his colleagues in the USA around the turn of the century, and a remedy of great power was put on the homeopathic map. Lachesis represents a flagship for the other snake remedies, because it is the best proven and because we have formidable clinical evidence of its healing capacities. By 'flagship', we mean that often when Lachesis repertorises well, other snake remedies would be better and certainly should be considered.

---

* Bedayn, G., 1992, "Lachesis: Metaphor [and Myth] as Medicine". The Homeopath, vol. 12/1

Competition

The original snakes were lizards. They lived in a time of intense competition—the age of dinosaurs. Reptilian evolution proceeded in three directions: the dinosaurs, who grew ever more gigantic; the birds, whose enlarged forelimbs provided wings; and the snakes, who lost their limbs while extending their backbone. Now slithering and slight, the snakes were able to penetrate deep into the earth, into the chasms, chambers and networks of caves that especially abound in limestone regions. This underground world was a great kingdom which, though teeming with life, had not yet been colonised by large and aggressive animals. The snakes therefore had no competitors in this new environment. Much later, or so palaeontologists believe, after the demise of dinosaurs, snakes re-emerged, many having evolved special apparatus for survival. They had now become mighty and feared, as the name Surukuku, 'the master of the bush', implies.

Homeopathic snake remedy types are extremely sensitive to rivalry. They either shun it or thrive within it. Those who thrive in competition stir up rivalry, while those who are victims of it shrink back. For instance, in a family with siblings, jealousy may loom large. Lachesis types develop cunning ways of manipulating the situation to get the upper hand. They listen keenly to what is happening. They have an ear to the emotional subtext in any dialogue, feeling who is where in the interplay of power, and how they can slip in on the winning side. Those who shrink from this emotional environment, even more keenly than those who engage in it, feel injured by their surroundings. Coupled with the sensation of constriction, feeling injured is the uncompensated state of the entire snake family.

Living in their realm of darkness, the snakes accentuated their senses of smell, touch and hearing. The snake tracks down its prey with its flickering forked tongue, which draws the smell towards the olfactory organs. Sound- and touch-sensitivity to low vibrations reveal the heartbeat of the prey. Moving stealthily within range, the venomous snake strikes rapidly, injecting a deadly poison that digests the prey from within. The neurotoxic element of the venom paralyses the prey so that it cannot escape. The haemolytic element, a development of the salivary glands, digests the blood. The snake swallows its quarry whole, dislocating its jaw so that it can 'walk' the victim into its mouth. These ideas are worth noting as we consider the sort of person for whom Lachesis is the remedy.

Left-sided

Everything about the Lachesis way is sinister, left-handed (sinister is Latin for left). In traditional theatre and pantomime, the villain enters stage left and the audience hiss. In Lachesis folk, the left side is most affected. It is the side that is weaker and first becomes ill. Indeed, the snake has its major internal organs on the left side. Lycopodium is right-sided, for people who use their keen intellect to dominate others, but with left-sided Lachesis, the means of getting the upper hand is primarily by manipulation, cunning, deceit and propaganda. They make wonderful orators and journalists, getting to the root of the matter and finding out everything that is wrong and bad.

Lachesis people are intense; they have over-active minds and are sharp-tongued, witty or satirical. They are often charismatic but they can be ruthless and remorseless too. Commonly they have a great command of languages: think of that flickering tongue! They are loquacious. They might even finish your sentence for you because they have already jumped to the conclusion you are driving towards—a kind of clairvoyance. At the other polarity, they can ramble and lose coherence, especially if they have drunk too much. Lachesis is a sterling remedy for old drunkards with purple complexions. We like to imagine a colourful aristocratic lady, with glittering tiara, wrapped in silks but with an open neck, surrounded by an entourage of flatterers, and given to fine wines and witty put-downs. And woe to those who cross her!

These types are strong-minded, opinionated, colourful, vivid and sometimes fanatical, especially about political, religious or ethical issues. They go passionately into fields where most fear to tread.

On the physical level, they are warm-blooded. Think of snakes basking in the sun to warm up their reptilian cold blood. Once warmed up, they have to avoid over-heating and slither away into the shade. All venomous snake remedies bleed easily. Lachesis is an important remedy for excessive menstruation and menopausal problems, especially hot flushes. Lachesis patients may present with spontaneous bruising where the disolouration is purple. This reminds us of the site of an actual bite because here too, the skin becomes mottled and purple. It amuses us to think of the similarity with a 'purple passage' in literature, because this style would suit a Lachesis author.

Lachesis is suited to florid personalities. We may find them in colourful occupations like theatre and film. Theatre happens on the street too, among tradespeople who bitch and barter, and in business and advertising—amongst those who put on displays, shows, and exhibitions, and who talk passionately and persuasively.

Just as the snake has to open its mouth wide to swallow its prey whole, so the Lachesis person likes to open their throat wide and get the words out in a great gush, enveloping you in their rhetoric. However, there may be a sense of choking and constriction in the throat. Almost always there is a great dislike of tight clothing or anything that creates constriction. Note that human snake-catchers, and animals that prey on snakes, grasp them around their neck because this is the only way of rendering them powerless to strike. Hence the neck is a vulnerable area for Lachesis types. Intolerance of cravats, scarves and roll necks, and sore throats and suppurating tonsils (often left-sided) are among common Lachesis pathologies. Touching the throat cannot be tolerated.

Restraint and constriction

Snakes usually shed their skins annually. We might say that they spend much of their time in clothing that is too tight. From time to time they burst through and become reborn in a new skin that fits them for a while, before it becomes too tight again. This is true both physically and psychologically. Lachesis is much worse for any kind of restraint. They need to burst out.

Transitions

A transition is a time when one must let go of the past and move on because we have outgrown our old situation; it has become constricting. Because Lachesis cannot bear restraint or constriction, it has a place during transitions: from winter to summer (worse in spring, when snakes come out of hibernation); from waking to sleeping (when they are suddenly awakened by panic, with a feeling of being choked or suffocated, and a bounding heart); and in the menopause, which marks the end of fertility. Menopause is the time when women often feel that they have lost their beauty, edge and attractiveness. They easily become jealous of rivals, daughters, anyone who may seem lovelier than they. Either they will strike out against them or they will slink into profound despondency and brooding silence. Taciturnity is the flip side to their more typical loquacity, and fits in with the picture of injured pride.

Lachesis people can be very sexual. However, once shacked up, they are the most possessive lovers and become insanely jealous when threatened. The Lachesis partner needs to hold his beloved in tightening coils of ownership. Despite this, or perhaps because of it, they can feel trapped in monogamy, and break free.

The male menopause is characterised by stupid behaviour, such as taking out an extra mortgage to buy a new sports car (the bird-puller), and indeed, pulling the bird. This man worries that he is losing his sexual prowess. Of equal importance are his relationships in the workplace. How do his colleagues view him? Is it all downhill from here? Lachesis types may express these doubts about themselves in physical pathology, typically the heart, and psychologically, in the form of one-upmanship. They can go into a depression, which is not as dark as Aurum, yet still potentially suicidal.

This is typically a time for Lachesis individuals to become attached to God. For Aurum individuals, praying is a last-ditch attempt to reconnect with the power of God as a personification of truth, honour, and dignity. In the case of Lachesis, the religious impulse has more to do with the need to calm down, to subdue the intensity of emotions, the turmoil of sexual heat. The Old Testament God, Yahweh, the giver of rules, the sustainer of moral values, He who quells sexual misdemeanour and other untoward excesses, the jealous God, could be a personification of the restrictive aspects of Lachesis—the stranglehold!

The serpent and Eden

In our culture, the serpent represents a malefic influence. Coiled around the apple tree of the knowledge of good and evil in the Garden of Eden, the serpent symbolises divine arrogance. He is the tempter through which humans gain knowledge, yet lose their hallowed place in the garden of plenty. The serpent is the Devil (D-evil), but he is also Lucifer, herald of light, who sits at the right hand of God. He tempts with the knowledge that will break up the unified world of Eden forever, because this knowledge operates by division and discrimination. The serpent asks Eve whether she and Adam would like to be as God and to know all that God knows. Though she is aware that the reasonable and '*right*' thing to do is to refuse the serpent's offer, Eve follows the *left*-hand path of instinct and eats the apple. When God, out and about in the cool of evening (snake-like, He shuns the heat of day), sees that Adam and Eve have covered their naked bodies with fig leaves, He knows they have transgressed. He needs to ensure that they won't get a chance to eat the fruit of the other tree, the tree of eternal life, and become immortal, as He is. Thus He banishes them from Eden. By this action he reveals his jealous aspect.

Let us examine Lachesis' *modus operandi*—the venom with the power to digest the victim from within, to degenerate its 'wholeness'. The left-hand path, the sinister way of Lachesis, is best symbolised by "?", probably the most snaky of our glyphs.* This is just how it works in practice. In Shakespeare's *Othello,* for example, Iago poisons Othello's mind with pointed questions, suggestions and innuendo, so that Othello reaches his own conclusion that his wife has been unfaithful to him on the flimsiest of evidence. Jealousy boils in his blood and erupts. Murder is the outcome.

The Lachesis inquiry can probe deeply, undermining the foundations of faith. The question mark can be placed upon any over-defined certainty. Who is God? What is eternity? Are you sure? Do you know? All these inquiries lead to uncertainty and, in so doing, reveal something of the true nature of existence.

---

* Thanks are due to Jürgen Becker for this observation

We can vividly picture Lachesis pathology, but can easily forget the Lachesis gift of clear vision—clairvoyance. The disintegration of certainty can lead to a new integration of self with eternity. In application, we might witness the resolution of jealousy or other wounding attachments in the direction of love.

Miasms

From the point of view of miasmatic analysis, the Syphilitic aspect of a Lachesis patient's pathology is perfectly portrayed in their delusion that their surroundings are injuring them; their single-minded attachment to one person; their monomaniacal jealousy of rivals; their determination to destroy any competitor; and physically, their haemorrhagic pathology. Sycotic traits can be seen in loquacity, boasting and sexual excess.

CHAPTER 15

MERCURIUS—DESTRUCTION AND CREATION, DECAY AND PURITY

A predominantly Syphilitic remedy

The Greek god Hermes and his Roman counterpart Mercury have an honoured place in the ancient pantheons. In astrology, the qualities of the planet Mercury and the signs it rules, Gemini and Virgo, include duplicity, activity, trading, communication, knowledge, and (in the case of Virgo) purity. As a personification and metaphor of the alchemical process, Mercurius stood for transformation and change, for the principle of life itself. In the preparation of the homeopathic remedies, we use Mercurius solubilis (dissolving, soluble) and Mercurius vivus (living, alive). As we shall see, mercury is the dissolving metal; it is also fluid and, in this sense, alive—hence its traditional name of quicksilver, meaning living silver. The theme of the dissolution of form leading to death is easy to find in Mercurius, while the opposite, new beginnings leading to life, is the promise which healing holds out.

When speaking of rubrics and symptoms, we make perhaps too small a distinction between the separate provings of Merc viv and Merc sol. Both bring out almost identical physical symptoms, but there are certain complementary mental symptoms, notably slowness of expression in the case of Merc viv and hurriedness in Merc sol (see Allen's *Encyclopaedia of Pure Materia Medica*). People for whom Merc sol is the simillimum typically have an earnest need to communicate, to talk, to amalgamate. But if they feel uncomfortable, as they often do ("delusion, surrounded by enemies"), they may present as uncommunicative (typically Merc viv), or may even wish to "get the hell out of the place".

Mercurius solubilis Hahnemannii, or dimercurous ammonium nitrate, was synthesised by Hahnemann the chemist before his discovery of the healing art of homeopathy as a substitute for the corrosive mercury salts in use at that time. As Clarke explains, "[Merc sol] was at once adopted in all countries on account of its much milder and more efficacious anti-Syphilitic qualities."

Nitrates are associated with plant growth. Forming the bulk of commercially produced fertilisers, they are responsible for lush and rapid growth and exemplify a general theme of expansion. Their oxidising properties are responsible for the 'fire' of most explosives. Gunpowder contains roughly 73% potassium nitrate. The nitrating of mercury probably accounts for the characteristic hurriedness and rapid speech of Merc sol, this being a quality of over-extension and expansion. The nitrating of silver gives the remedy Arg nit its speediness and 'enlargement' of imagination, including anticipatory anxieties as well as delusions and sensations of enlargement. The high explosive nitroglycerine, made into the remedy Glonoinum, gives characteristic confusion, delusions and sensations of enlargement, surgings of blood and pulsation sensations in head, heart and throughout the body. So, again, we need to make the distinction between the two mercurius preparations: if the patient is secretive and silent, then Merc viv will suit, whereas the more vivacious and talkative types do better on Merc sol.

Mercury is unique among metals in that it is in a liquid state at room temperatures. This feature is exploited in the manufacture of thermometers, sphygmomanometers and other measurement apparatus. Kent describes the patient who needs Mercurius as a human barometer. Clarke writes:

> There was a fitness in naming this metal after the volatile deity. It provides us with weather-glasses and thermometers, and it turns those who are under its influence into weather-glasses and thermometers likewise. (An electrician, who at one time was required to work with his hands frequently in a trough filled with quicksilver, thereafter could not bear the slightest shock of electricity, though before he could stand very strong ones.) And herein lies one of the grand characteristics of the remedy: as the thermometer is sensitive to changes either to hot or cold, so is the Merc patient. Other remedies are predominantly one or the other: Merc is both—worse by heat and worse by cold.

George Vithoulkas writes:

The basic idea is that there is a lack of reactive power coupled with an instability or inefficiency of function.

Should a mercury thermometer bulb be smashed, the mercury scatters widely in a myriad tiny droplets. We may recall the ensuing scramble on all fours to insure that all droplets are gathered up. We know from clinical experience as well as by analogy that those patients for whom Mercurius is the remedy cannot keep themselves together when stressed physically, and that they undergo mental torment when under real or imagined attack. In the Generalities section of the Repertory, Mercurius is mentioned in fifty-five rubrics of aggravation and in only seven of amelioration!

Amalgamating, transforming and destroying

Another legendary aspect of mercury lies in its capacity to amalgamate with other substances. This property is extensively used in the extraction of gold from low-grade ores. Anyone unfortunate enough to have lost a ring of silver or gold to mercury will have observed this phenomenon, as will those who suffer mercury poisoning when amalgam fillings break down.

The amalgam used for fillings is produced by combining mercury with other metals. At first this amalgam is soft but soon hardens to form a plug. However, this plug, far from being inert, is in fact reactive and is broken down not only by the grinding action of chewing but also by fruit acids—eating a grapefruit for breakfast releases quantities of deadly mercury salts. To make matters worse, fillings put in at different times using slightly differing proportions of amalgamating metals have mismatching electrochemical properties. This leads to mercury salts leaching out and being ingested. Unfortunately this can present a serious health hazard, because mercury is one of the most potent inorganic poisons. It has the capacity to enter readily into organic molecules. For this reason it also gains access to the human organism through concentration up the food chain, when we eat fish and animals living in polluted environments. It also may be inhaled as fumes; it moves out of a solid into a liquid state at room temperature, and with equal ease passes into a vaporous state.

The god Hermes reflected mercury's transformative character as messenger of the gods at the tender age of three days, when he changed himself into a mist, slipped under the door of his room and reformed himself on the other side. Hermes had the unique ability amongst the Olympian gods to enter Hades, the underworld, and guide the souls of the dead. His passport into Hades was stamped with the Mercurial marks of the capacity for transformation. In other words, Hermes is able to amalgamate with diverse and opposing states and properties, entering into all aspects of life and death with equal ease. Mercurius is an appropriate remedy in situations of decomposition, putrefaction and decay, promoting a veritable meltdown of tissues.

Mercury destroys life by ulceration and necrosis. When it falls on the surface of another metal with which it has an amalgamating affinity, it eats into it. The area of contact first becomes fluid, then ulcerates, and finally is incorporated into an amalgam. Mercurius is the Syphilitic medicine par excellence. The collapsed nasal septum is well known amongst old syphilitic patients, wherefrom, by means of psychic mirroring, we obtain the symptoms "pulls one's nose in the street" and "takes people by the nose." Death by necrosis is mercury's fundamental note. Its manner of pathologising may be summed up by the word 'decomposition'. Clarke writes:

> We of the present generation can hardly form a conception of the havoc wrought by Mercury in the days when it was considered necessary to "touch the gums" in all cases for which Mercury was prescribed before any good could be hoped for. The motto, "Salivation is Salvation", tells its own tale... For a graphic picture of a practice which was part of the ordinary routine until recent times, I quote the following from Bransby Cooper's First Lines of Surgery, 6th ed., p348: "Mercury acts upon some individuals like a poison: they are seized with palpitations of the heart, tremblings of the limbs, oppression of the breathing, and irregular pulse. When such indisposition takes place in a person employing Mercury we

2

conclude that this mineral is actually producing a deleterious impression on the system. It was noticed by the late Mr Pearson that every year, when it was the custom to salivate freely, a certain number of individuals thus treated died suddenly in the Lock Hospital. They were first affected as I have described, and, on attempting to make the slightest effort they dropped down dead. Mr Pearson learned from experience that these deaths arose from the deleterious action of Mercury on the constitution, and the derangement of the system thus excited he proposed to call the Mercurial erethismus.

Eaten by worms

Mercurius is the only remedy in the rubrics, "delusion, fancied living things were creeping into mouth at night" and "delusion, living things were creeping into vagina at night", reminiscent of the buried corpse in the "night" of the coffin. Another unique symptom, "delusion, body made of sweets", may be interpreted in the light of the characteristic sweet smell of death (before the rank rotting), and of sweet things attracting flies. Images of maggots or faeces come to the mind of certain Mercurius patients—Mercury and Veratrum are the shit eaters of the Materia Medica! We have had patients who were cured only with Mercurius who have had a pathological horror of such things, or have recurrent nightmares focusing upon such imagery. There may be disgust of life and loathing of self in a manner similar to Lac caninum.

In such cases, escape may be the survival strategy adopted—actually being 'on the run', or in fantasy, flying on mercurial wings into a dreamscape. One patient, previously prescribed Lac caninum with only ameliorative results, had suffered abuse from her older, pathologically jealous sibling during her entire childhood; later, she was sexually abused also. Mercurius proved to be her simillimum. In order to escape, she wanted to be a fairy, to fly away out of what she described as "the dead world of my invaded self." This image gives us a sense of what Margaret Tyler called "the inwardness of drugs". It is reminiscent of the Syphilitic and AIDS miasms.

Even in an early stage of physical Mercurius pathology, we expect to find symptoms associated with rot and decay, such as excessive and fetid salivation, offensive perspiration, glandular swelling, ulceration with no tendency to heal, dysenteric, bloody stools and associated mental symptoms of disgust or hostility. When the psyche is primarily affected, the patient may feel impelled to touch things in order to keep the pervading sense of loathing and evil at bay. The old school used mercurial salts in the war against that evil and dirty disease, syphilis. "Washing, always, her hands" had previously been, in Kent's repertory, a symptom of Syphilinum only.

It is clear from the Mind section of the Repertory that many cardinal symptoms of Mercurius are contained within the Delusions section. The majority of these relate to crimes, enemies, injuries, dangerous animals, mutilation and thieves, while the rubric "escape, attempts to" further highlights the unstable and paranoid state of mind. These internal motifs of persecution and destruction are expressed outwardly as impulses to destroy. This is so because any sustained state of the inner being, any frozen psychological posture, is compensated for by a reciprocal and opposite gesture towards the world. The inner state is both expressed and protected by the outer opposite activity or façade.

Weaponry

As high explosives began to take over from gunpowder, a suitably forcible detonator was sought, and the fulminate of mercury was found. This is a highly unstable compound requiring only a low-velocity impact to detonate—reminiscent of the anger of Mercurius patients who easily fire off at the slightest provocation. It is the high molecular density of mercury that makes this detonator so effective at triggering a bomb. Fulminate of mercury is still used today in warfare to initiate the explosion of bombs, though it has been replaced in gun cartridges because of its toxicity.

The Synthetic Repertory lists eleven sub-rubrics to the major rubric "kill, desire to" in which Mercurius appears. Knives and razors figure frequently. In the light of this Syphilitic posture, we can appreciate why Mercurius is the only remedy listed in bold type in the rubric "anarchist, revolutionary". It also appears in "moral feeling, want of" and "criminal, disposition to become, without remorse". Naturally, this state of mind represents an advanced state of pathological breakdown and it is unusual for patients such as these to come into the consulting room. Yet certain politicians and dictators may have needed Mercurius.

Certainly these trends may be revealed in the troubled dreams which assail such patients. The following, from the Dreams section of MacRepertory, are some of them:

> *DREAMS: bitten, animals, by; blood; mangled remains; boars, wild; dead bodies; disgusting; dogs, bitten, by, of being; drowning; fire; flood; frightful; hideous; murdered, of being; quarrels; revolution; riot; robbers; shooting; swallowing pins; water; danger from; water; falling into; water; flood, of a.*

Isolation

Another Mercurius feature often met with in the consulting room, which may be associated with the deepest Aurum-like self-deprecation, sense of failure and self-loathing, is guilt and shame. Associated with this self-condemnation is a feeling of total isolation.

A patient for whom Mercurius proved curative described his feelings of desolation and isolation thus: "My worst nightmare is that I will be in hell, totally isolated and condemned, with no one to help me." His deepest horror was of madness. He feared that he would go on a rampage and bludgeon everyone to death. His relief came from listening to music. During his teens he isolated himself from his peers, locked himself in his room and listened to morbid music, "the more morbid the better". During progress to cure the pathology moved from the psychological level to the physical: he developed a foul mouth and a patchy, dirty, discoloured tongue. The rubric, "delusion, everyone is an enemy" helps us to understand that for a Mercurius type in such a state, the only safe haven is to be alone. Platina is also to be found in this rubric and is known to be one of the most 'alone' remedies in the Materia Medica.

Mutability and form

The theme of Mercurius is associated with its uniqueness as the fluid metal, coupled with its amalgamating propensity. Out of this signature we may easily extract the concepts of instability, mutability, necrosis and decay—the ultimate mutation of life into death. In order to keep fluidity, insecurity, attack and decay at bay, Mercurius patients may adopt the survival strategy of developing precision in their activities and meticulous order in their lives—an overriding need for stability of form. This is exemplified by a fanatical attention to detail and extreme conscientiousness about trifles in perhaps just one aspect of their lives, for instance, cleanliness and hygiene, or perfection of style. The latter was developed by one Mercurius patient, a master in the martial arts, to a far greater degree than was necessary for overwhelming an assailant.

Mercurius and politicians

As intimated earlier, certain politicians may have needed Mercurius. It seems appropriate that the positive qualities exemplified by Hermes the mediator and the fair-spoken should be taken up and projected by a spokesman of the people. The god Mercury was associated with tradesmen, with whom the gift of the gab is all-important, and Mercurius the medicine has an elective affinity for the throat, the chief centre of speech and communication. A politician who was truly a messenger of the gods would be a boon to humanity, but as has been said, "Power corrupts (an apt phrase to describe Mercurius), and absolute power corrupts absolutely". Certain politicians who have been seduced by power are affected by the Mercurius *hubris.* That is, they may come to believe that they are the sun itself, rather than the sun's messenger. It is the height of *hubris* to believe that one is a god!

Given Napoleon's Mercurius habits of twitching and jerking and his tendency to take people by the nose, it is small wonder that he kept his hand tucked away in his jacket. Napoleon would perhaps have been aided in his aims had he taken Mercurius; indeed, that might well have also helped him to more clearly perceive and execute his aims. Perhaps he would have become 'a nicer guy'. It is conjectured that his paranoia and fear of surprise attack gave rise to his inability to create an effective chain of command, all major decisions being solely dependent upon himself. It is known that the pain of his piles (the haemorrhoids of Mercurius are legendary) kept him from mounting his steed, surveying battle, and being civil to his officers, and may well have cost him victory at Waterloo.

Saddam Hussein is another possible case of Mercurius. However, as we have no account of Saddam's feelings, we can only speculate about his state and simillimum.

Revolutionaries

In her book *Relating,* Liz Greene writes, "Mercury is the Sun's messenger, and while the sun is the symbol of the essence, Mercury is the symbol of that function which enables us to know the essence." In order to realise a new beginning, and to be informed (an astrologically mercurial influence in a chart), a revolutionary must have clarity of vision. The Mercurius revolutionary is driven by the felt need to obliterate the old corruption (which fills him with profound disgust) and replace it with something pure and new. In his view, the end justifies the means, albeit violent revolution.

The greatest anti-Syphilitic remedy, Mercurius, is a perfect homeopathic fit for the planning and the battle phases of conflict: it is not necessarily so, though, for the immediate effects of the ravages of war, when acute fear predominates and such remedies as Aconite, Stramonium, Opium or Ferrum phos might be more frequently indicated. During hostilities, astrologers will recognise Martian, Uranian and Plutonian motifs.

To recapitulate, the patient for whom Mercurius is the simillimum is eaten away from within as is a corpse, auto-digested from the rotting guts outwards towards the periphery. He is the guilty criminal, the shit eater who is filled with disgust and self-loathing, who is in hell, who is surrounded by enemies, who fights or flees. If this type is compensated and functioning, he does so by adhering to a dogma or a fixed form (Mercurius has been added to the rubric "monomania").

Everything in nature may be viewed from two sides. In the case of Mercurius, these two aspects are symbolised by the black and white, snake-entwining caduceus of Hermes, the staff that symbolises healing. The portrait of Mercurius derived from toxicological and proving evidence is the pathological downside of the messenger of the gods, the carrier of the pure light of truth and life, the 'vivus' principle. Just as Mercury corrupts, so it may also elevate, raising the spirit of humanity out of filth into purity. It can do this because of its essentially fluid and amalgamating nature, and its ability to experience things by entering into their opposing qualities, their two sides. Mercurius people may rise to act out the life of the messenger of the gods and be a communicator of life-and-death principles.

Mercurius persons may be filled with bubbly enthusiasm for life, desiring to make deep and intimate connections with people and society. They often retain childlike 'Peter Pan' qualities. Hermes is portrayed as a young man with wings on his heels, whereas other gods are older and wiser. In Kent's Repertory, Mercurius is the single remedy in the rubric "precocity". In the presence of Mercurial people acting from a healthy centre, we are reminded of the winged deity, the messenger making instantaneous connections, having precocious cognitive skills, and rapid, often mellifluous speech. Such persons show great receptivity to all stimuli; their antennae are always out. They often find a place in the family or in society as entertainers, performers and mimics, taking on many personae with greatest dexterity. These aspects of the Mercurius personality are most clearly seen in children, though naturally, they may also live out the downside, especially in adolescence.

Mercury and Syphilis

Mercury's Syphilitic nature has its physical expression in its tendency to ulceration, pus, and decay. The psychological imperative is also to keep death at bay. The Mercurius type may attempt this by developing a monomania about purity (absence of corruption), for example, fundamentalism. The concern with purity can manifest as a positive quality: they may pursue any creative activity with a determination to get everything in place and just right.

CHAPTER 16

TARENTULA HISPANICA—BOUND UP YET COMPELLED TO MOVE

A Tubercular miasm remedy

Tarentula hispanica, the Spanish spider, belongs to the Tarentula family and is a member of the *Lycosa tarentula,* wolf spider, group. It is a large, hairy spider that lives alone in a burrow. Although some of the Tarentula family have brightly coloured markings on their body, this member does not. It is fiercely territorial and will attack any intruder into its territory. The female only gets together with a male for mating, and if he approaches her when she is not in the mood, or if she mates with him but then feels hungry, she may kill and eat him.

The babies of the Tarentula hispanica are independent from birth, but the mother spider binds them up in silk to stop them wandering. Considering that the babies will grow into aggressive predators that catch their prey by running, bounding and jumping, these silk bonds must be a maddening restriction. To put it another way, restriction would be a primary sensation from which running and pouncing would be secondary attributes. These feelings arise when Tarentula characteristics are translated though the provers into human terms.

The Tarentula catches its prey—which may be much bigger than itself—by hiding in the entrance of the burrow while the prey passes. It then bounds after it, jumps on it from behind, and bites it on the back of the neck. Through its fangs it injects a neurotoxin into its ganglia to paralyse it. It lets it go, quickly retreats into its burrow, and waits for the poison to take effect. The venom liquefies the prey's insides, so that the spider can suck them out. It is an almost instantaneous rotting process. Hence the remedy is effective in states of sepsis.

Foxiness

Tarentula types are 'foxy', deceptive and cunning by nature, as expected of a spider that hunts by stealth. The alternation of violent or aggressive behaviour with cowardice is a feature of this remedy. Tarentula types fear being assaulted, injured and trapped themselves, but inflict hurts on others. Typical Tarentula behaviour in a child might be for her to creep out of her hiding place and create mischief when no one is looking, then, when someone looks, to retreat and hide, while keeping a furtive eye on the effect she is producing. Tarentula has sly destructive movements combined with an incredible quickness; she jumps out of bed and smashes something before she can be prevented. This kind of behaviour, followed by a protestation of innocence, is a specific of the remedy. Tarentula types are capable of feigning sickness or a fainting fit to serve their own ends or to get attention.

Restless movement and hurry

Tarantulas can run very fast, and a Tarentula keynote is hurry and restlessness. The remedy has the symptom, "great haste in whatever I undertook, from constant fear that something would happen to prevent my finishing it" (Allen). When the spider catches its prey, it must inject its poison into exactly the right place on the prey or risk being killed by it.

The venom of this spider has an affinity with the nervous system, resulting in bizarre physical restlessness and uncontrolled agitation. Traditionally, it was believed that the person who was bitten by the spider went into a state known as tarentism, a fit of wild singing and dancing with extravagant behaviour and loss of control. The condition was cured by bringing in musicians to play fast, rhythmic music so that the bite victim would dance himself into a sweaty state of exhaustion. However, the condition was thought to return each year on the same day, when the music cure would have to be repeated (Tarentula can have yearly periodicity). The dance called the tarantella was named after the manic dancing of bite victims.

In reality, however, it is unlikely that a Tarentula bite would have such extreme and long-lasting effects. A theory has emerged that the widespread belief in tarentism may have been used as a convenient excuse to break out of societal and religious constraints! The belief emerged in Spain at a time when Catholicism imposed a political and social rule upon the people, which today is difficult for us to comprehend. Thus the phenomenon of tarentism may be more about Tarentula needing to break out of constraints by foxy means rather than any real effects of the venom. In respect of breaking out of societal or family traps, Tarentula has correspondences to Tuberculinum.

Tarentula types must walk about, but walking aggravates; they are better for relaxation. They can run better than they can walk. There may be a feeling as if they cannot control their legs, as if they do not obey their will. They walk and work fast. Others move and work too slowly for them. They have the famed industriousness of the spider and watching them at work is like seeing someone with more than just one pair of hands; often they will do more than one thing at a time. They must be busy. Time passes too slowly for Tarentulas. There is no place of rest and they may even sleepwalk.

Tarentula's restlessness is especially obvious in the arms and legs, as befits a spider remedy. There may be involuntary gestures as if knitting; unceasing movement; constant jerking, trembling and twitching; hands and fingers that are never still; or rolling the head or body from side to side. Often, there are spasms or strange, repeated gestures with a circular motion, like a spider's legs as they move. These movements can be vehement. A Tarentula baby may kick out with his feet constantly—as if against the silk bonds with which mother Tarantulas bind their young. It is a common remedy for hyperactive children.

A case comes to mind of a baby who continually kicked and pushed his mother away. Feeding had become a major struggle—when he fed he bit her nipples—and he was losing weight. He looked wild and very skinny. The situation at conception shed light upon the case. His parents were living in cramped accommodation and though they wanted a family later, he was unplanned and they felt unready for him. His mother spent the first trimester asking him to go away, but her 'prayer' for a spontaneous miscarriage went unanswered. She had not the heart to force the issue and therefore submitted herself to her fate, becoming increasingly desperate and hysterical. She could not bear touch or even the pressure of bedclothes—sleeping under only a sheet. She was most sensitive over her abdomen, and felt very anxious there. She took it out on her husband, hit him, bit him and threatened to kill him. She swept all the dishes off the sink onto the floor. Her husband discovered that music calmed her when she was hysterical—dance music! Going further back into her history revealed deep animosity between her and her own mother. She felt trapped, restrained and dominated by her mother, yet unable to break away until late in her teens. She felt small, literally, as if her body were diminished. She was sensitive to even mild criticism, felt deeply insulted, and had to restrain herself from violence. In the sixth form, she transformed herself from a cowed character into a loud-mouth. She became the school eccentric, dressed in brightest colours, wanted to be lead singer in the rock band, and wrote wild lyrics. Yet unfortunately for her, she alienated everyone by her antics. She was very pushy, forcing others to speed up all the time. She said that they couldn't keep up with her. She suffered a car crash and head injury. Convulsions and rages followed—throwing things and biting. These were 'successfully' treated by drugs and she calmed down and got married to a musician.

If the increased activity and restless movement seen in this type is not sufficient to relieve the over-stimulation of the nerves, Tarentula can move into a manic or hysterical state. They can display violence or rage comparable to Belladonna and Stramonium. Tarentula's insanity is accompanied by abnormal strength, just as the Tarantula spider can tackle and eat prey bigger than itself.

The opposite pole of Tarentula's restlessness is paralysis—another effect of the spider's venom. Rigidity and muscle cramps can be accompanied by weakness, trembling, and numbness. Skin symptoms can include violent itching or numbness.

Another case had a woman with a multiple sclerosis diagnosis. She suffered from numbness of the skin as well as unsteady gate and overall weakness. Each morning she would endure involuntary gyrations of her legs for about one hour—they would wind and unwind in slow motion, after which, with the support of callipers (metal supports), she could venture forth. In her teenage she had loved to play electronic game machines. She said that she was a match for any boy—she made mincemeat of them. She had been a tomboy and enjoyed challenges of danger and speed; everything had to be done at a breakneck pace. As a *coup de grace* she confessed to eating sand well into her childhood! (This is a peculiar Tarentula symptom which connects with the spider's habitat—a hole in the ground.)

Sensory hypersensitivity and excitement

In Tarantula poisoning, the senses become excessively sensitive: light and noise aggravate. The spider has four eyes and good eyesight. It is, however, photophobic (like many patients needing the remedy) and avoids direct sunlight. Tarentula headaches may be accompanied by photophobia.

Tarentula people have intense visual imaginations. When they close their eyes, they may have horrible visions of monsters or diabolical faces. They also have delusions of insects, or natural spider horrors of having their legs cut off and of being small.

Tarentula is especially sensitive to strong colours like red, yellow, green and black; there may be an aversion or desire for these colours, which feature on the bodies of other members of the Tarentula family. If a patient in a Tarentula delirium sees someone wearing clothes whose colour is displeasing, the patient must escape, for the sight worsens his anguish and aggravates all the symptoms. Tarantulas are territorial and may react strongly to these colours because they associate them with the approach of an intruder.

The spider's sense of touch, transmitted via the legs to the head and body, is so sensitive that it can feel the vibrations of a prey animal approaching and judge whether it is sufficiently small to overcome. The tips of Tarentula types' fingers are very sensitive. They may be very averse to being touched as it feels like too much stimulation. On the other hand, they are better for continued rubbing and massage, as this neutralises the over-sensitivity.

Both the Tarantula spider and Tarentula people have exaggeratedly strong hearing, since the spider locates its prey by sound and vibration. Tarentula types may be able to hear a particular person whisper across a crowded room, or hear what people inside a building are saying while they are outside.

Music

They are exquisitely sensitive to music either positively or negatively, depending on its type and the likes of the individual. In general, they respond compulsively to fast and rhythmic music, and are compelled to dance to it. Music alleviates the restlessness of the extremities. Sepia types also love to dance, but for different reasons: their sluggish system is ameliorated by the activity, though because of this sluggishness it may take some effort to get started. Tarentula has no choice: he is itching to get up and dance the minute the right kind of music starts. This sensitivity to rhythm reflects the spider's sensitivity to the footfalls of approaching prey.

Suddenness and violence

Tarentula's mood changes are as sudden as the spider's switch from quiet waiting to pouncing on its prey: gaiety and laughter turn to sudden spitefulness. He also has immoderate sardonic, mocking laughter, which may lead to screaming; or destructive mania followed by laughter and apologies.

Tarentula's symptoms are violent and sudden in onset, like the predatory behaviour of the spider. He may strike himself and others, tear and rend and destroy. In insanity, he may threaten death and destruction (a singular symptom). This relates both to the poisonous, predatory nature of the spider and the mythological association of spiders with prediction of death. The Great Mother, in her aspect as weaver of destiny and fate, is sometimes depicted as a spider.

Attention-seeking

The Tarentula spider decorates the entrance to its burrow with silk, perhaps linking with the desire of Tarentula types to decorate themself with bright and attractive clothing. They may have a deep aversion to the colour black, the colour of the spider itself.

Underlying the Tarentula rubric "ailments from disappointed love" lies a feeling that they not attractive enough and do not get the attention they crave. Their fondness for fast and wild dancing and love of bright colours is partly motivated by a desire to be noticed. It may also be sexually alluring—bright colours and dancing displays occur in many animals during the mating season.

Territorial behaviour

Tarentulas are strongly territorial. Tarentula types fear being approached and are over-sensitive to having their space invaded. Conversely, they may "crash" other people's space or boundaries, and some Tarantula spiders do not make a fixed home of their own but take over the territory of another spider.

The Tarantula spider is a loner, and Tarentula types are usually averse to company. However, they also fear to be alone.

Strange habits and symptoms

Tarentula types may feel sad after sexual excitement—perhaps a reference to the female Tarantula's habit of killing her mate after coition! The spider's sexual predatory nature is seen in Tarentula's tendency to extreme sexual excitement and nymphomania, which is aggravated by coition. Tarentula has sensitive genitals: men are prone to testicular swellings and women to dry, hot, raw, itching vulva and vagina.

Physical symptoms

Pains are sudden and violent in onset. There may be neuralgias, as if thousands of needles were pricking, as befits a remedy made from a neurotoxic, paralysing venom. The patient may roll from side to side in agony, or seem about to choke or suffocate (Tarentula is better for fresh air). His cough may be suffocating, accompanied by restlessness and screaming. If the patient has Tonsillitis, where he finds it hard to breathe because his neck is so swollen, he can respond well to Tarentula.

Choking sensations are a major feature of poisoning from a Tarentula bite: when the poison reaches the neck, a dark red or purple swelling appears. When choking seems imminent, a nosebleed with dark clots begins and relieves the symptoms. Even when well, Tarentula, like Lachesis, is aggravated by tight clothing around the neck.

Other conditions typical of the remedy are deep abscesses and carbuncles where the skin is purple, and swollen lymph glands, all similar to symptoms of the spider's bite.

Tarentula has a highly sensitive spine; a touch there will resonate and produce spasmodic pain throughout their bodies, just as the spider's whole body feels a stimulus anywhere in the vicinity.

Since this remedy has an affinity with over-stimulated states, it is not surprising that it strongly affects the cardiovascular system. Anxiety may be associated with tumultuous palpitation.

The remedy is useful for fibrous cancerous or benign tumours which have the appearance of a spider.

Miasms

Tarentula's deceptive nature and destructiveness are obviously Syphilitic. The mentality is primitive in that there is no tendency to cover up their mischief. It is as if the destructiveness is so extreme as to obliterate any self-regarding higher consciousness. The Tubercular miasm is noted for its Syphilitic content, while the distinctive key signature is the need to violently break out of restraining influences. As this perfectly describes the Tarentula state, we can see that the Tubercular miasm is dominant in this remedy.

A note on Tarentula cubensis

The remedy Tarentula cubensis is made from a Tarentula specimen that rotted before it was potentised. It is indicated in cases characterised by perpetual motion combined with physical disturbance.

Because the source material was not merely dead but rotting, it is useful in severe septic states and cases of boils with blueness of the skin—a precursor to the necrosis that occurs in septic states. The boil will likely be accompanied by agonising burning pain.

Tarentula cubensis, like Arsenicum, has been used in cases of dying patients where the 'flesh walks off' the person, to bring peace and ease the transition into death.

CHAPTER 17

TUBERCULINUM—RESTLESS DISCONTENT
A Syphilo-Psoric nosode (representing the Tubercular miasm)

A nosode is a homeopathic preparation of the product of disease. For example, Medorrhinum is made from gonorrhoeal discharge, and therefore contains gonococcus bacteria and vanquished leukocytes—the corpses of the immune defence agents. Carcinosin is prepared from various human cancers. Tuberculinum (of Kent) is prepared from the tubercular gland of a cow, while Bacillinum (of Burnett) is prepared from the sputum of a tubercular human.

A nosode is not identical with the miasm of its name. It may seem to hold out a false promise of curing these ancient tendencies, whereas in fact it is simply a remedy like any other. It is prescribed because of its similarity to the case, and exceptionally as an intercurrent remedy in a 'stuck' case.* However, a study of the nosodes through the provings and their clinical expressions does give us an insight into the miasms. Miasms represent archetypal disturbances of the vital force, just as polycrest remedies do.

The lost homeland

The Tuberculinum nosode is associated in a homeopath's mind with restless discontent. It is derived from a disease that arises in dispossessed populations and societies. People who have experienced this tragedy feel as if their heart is stuck in the record groove of the past and is singing the song of longing for the lost homeland: they are always looking for it, comparing the new against the old and finding the new wanting. Therefore, we find them restlessly searching for (but not finding) a new home and culture. Since the disease is associated with violent upheavals such as war, famine and subsequent conditions of deprivation, its miasmatic influence is primarily Syphilitic, although Psora (characterised by forsaken feeling, poverty and introspection) is also apparent.

---

* See Chapter 5, Miasms in clinical practice, "Prescribing methodologies".

Just as Tuberculinum's link with their homeland is broken, so they tend to go against the prevailing order, whether set by parents, school or society. The stereotypical Tuberculinum image is of an adolescent who needs to break away from home, and probably does so amidst quarrels. He seeks to find a new life, and travels restlessly from place to place in discontent and defiance. In this traveller's knapsack we may find a few treasured books of poetry, pornography and a ration of smoked meat! The latter is a well-known craving which can be linked to the fact that preserved meat is the ideal traveller's ration.

Tuberculinum suffers from being restricted, hemmed in or trapped. He may use the term "suffocated" to describe how he feels in such a situation. Physically, too, he suffers symptoms of suffocation in the form of various diseases of the lung and respiratory tract. Asthma, recurrent coughs, and bouts of pneumonia, pleurisy and bronchitis are strong indicators of the Tubercular miasm. He feels much better for open air and worse for being in a stuffy room.

Tuberculinum also has an affinity with the heart. One of the injunctions given to inexperienced prescribers is never to give high potencies of Tuberculinum to those with heart conditions, lest the patient has a heart attack. People who have lost their homeland grow heartsick. Two feelings are conjoined here: homesickness and forsaken feeling.

Tubercular types have a tendency to develop allergies. We can understand this on the basis that the individual has become used to one set of substances (his homeland) from which he is currently excluded. Just as he is being treated as a foreigner, so he is surrounded by substances that his body treats as foreign.

Kent advised that annual hay fever be treated with a yearly dose of Psorinum, but some modern practitioners recommend that it be treated by doses of Tuberculinum. This takes account of miasmatic development over time and major wars. As an aside, we must point out that although we have engaged in this practice for many years, this has rendered far from positive results. In our experience, nosodes should be treated as any other homeopathic remedy, i.e. on the basis of their similarity to the centre of the case. Of course, if the case is Tuberculinum, then Tuberculinum will be the angel of mercy.

Tuberculinum has certain characteristics in common with Carcinosin: most notably, love of travel, destructive temper, obstinacy, and marked revolutionary tendencies. Both Tuberculinum and Carcinosin children can be hyperactive as well as destructive. It may seem as if they are driven by Old Nick (the devil) himself to do things which are guaranteed to attract major disapproval. When this disapproval rains down upon them, it merely results in escalating destructive behaviour. Possible end results are terms in borstal (young offenders institution) or prison, to drug addiction, and, if they are fortunate, the rehabilitation centre.

Miasms

Two of Hahnemann's miasms are represented in Tuberculinum: Syphilis the destroyer and Psora the connector. In Compton Burnett's practice (early 20th century) the two remedies most frequently used by him were Tuberculinum and Thuja. In our times, the Tubercular miasm is thriving, not only as an emerging epidemic amongst immigrants, but also as a trend in young people. In other words, the predisposition has been, and is being, passed from generation to generation. The Tubercular miasm may be put into a nutshell as: 'my connection with the past has been destroyed; therefore I seek the new and kick the old'.

Two remedies presented in this book are representative of the Tubercular miasm: Tarentula and Rhus tox. The latter is also representative of the AIDS miasm.

CHAPTER 18

CARCINOSIN—CONFORMITY AND REBELLION

A Syco-Syphilitic nosode (representing the Cancer miasm)

The original Carcinosin, made from breast cancer tissue, was written about by Burnett and Clarke. Both used it widely as an intercurrent remedy in cases of active cancer. Closer to our time, Foubister (also working with the original Carcinosin) extended our knowledge of the remedy through his study of children born of parents who had suffered cancer. Carcinosin was for him what Sulphur had been for Hahnemann. He usually began his treatments with it, allowing its action to be completed before prescribing other remedies. He felt that the Cancer miasm, rather than Psora, was prevalent in our time.

Sources

Today, different preparations of Carcinosin are available, taken from various sources. There has been much debate about which preparation of Carcinosin acts best. In our experience, however, the homeopathic preparation of one type of cancer tissue behaves no differently from any other type.

Two provings carried out at the School of Homeopathy on the AIDS nosode throw light on this question of differently sourced preparations of Carcinosin. Two different remedies were made from the blood of two patients who subsequently died of fully blown AIDS. Each group took the remedy made from the different source. The aim was to find out whether the individuality of the people from whom the blood samples were taken influenced the outcome of the proving, i.e. whether the blood from one AIDS sufferer produced the same proving themes as the blood from another. They were found to be essentially alike. Similar experiments have been carried out with potentised human milk from different sources. The results from the differently sourced remedies were essentially the same. There is no reason to suppose that Carcinosin is any different in this respect from the AIDS nosode or Lac humanum/maternum.

What does the clamour over the origin of Carcinosin tell us about the remedy? Why have not homeopaths made a fuss about the sourcing of other remedies? The question is the same one that surrounds the *genus epidemicus* or remedy of an epidemic: does the disease so overwhelm the individuality of the different people affected that one remedy suited to the disease as a whole can cure all cases? Or does individuality win out, requiring a different remedy for each case? The consensus of opinion is that within one epidemic, there is one remedy that suits most cases. Similarly, the issue with Carcinosin is whether the energy of one potentised disease tissue *conforms* to the energy of cancer as a whole— flagging up the central Carcinosin polarity of conformity and rebellion. In our experience, each of the different versions of Carcinosin does conform to a Carcinosin norm and reveals the same essential themes. This argument is no different than would apply to any other remedy or material. It is given here because the debate seems to be driven not by impartial factors but by the intrinsic Carcinosin theme.

Conformity and rebellion

Cancerous tumours are characterised by an over-abundant proliferation of cells of one type. Cancer cells are regressive, having reverted to a less differentiated state than normal cells. Within the tumour, each cell conforms to its neighbour like bricks in a wall. However, from the point of view of the organism as a whole, the cells are rebellious and unruly. There is an escalating struggle between the body, which wishes to maintain its integrity and proper functioning, and the tumour, which subverts.

Cancer cells are like a monoculture. In a healthy organism, groups of differing cells cooperate together, while in cancerous tissue, the conformity of structure within the tumour allows no functional interfacing with surrounding tissues. Although it is genetically conforming (and can therefore bypass normal immune defence strategies), it is foreign (rebellious).

Tumours usually grow greedily and produce more waste products than the body can easily deal with. Gerson and other detox therapies have been successfully used in chronic diseases, including cancer, because they help the body rid itself of waste products and use its strength to fight the disease rather than clean the sewer. This aspect of cancer has a Psoric undertone, in that the body lacks the strength to purify itself. Obviously, toxic overload is not the only reason why cancer is so dangerous to the body. The other reasons are that:

- bodily systems fail because they are taken over by the cancer (a Syphilitic overtone)
- obstruction occurs due to growth of the tumour (a Sycotic overtone).

Miasms

The cancerous tendency thrives in a soil in which two miasms, Sycosis (proliferative tendencies) and Syphilis (destructive tendencies), combine, though some commentators suggest that all three miasms are represented. As Elizabeth Wright Hubbard put it, "Cancer is a marriage of the three miasms, with Alumina as the best man." In the 1950s, when Hubbard and Margaret Tyler (see Tyler's 'Alumina' in *Homeopathic Drug Pictures*) were practising and writing, aluminium—a primarily anti-Psoric remedy—was considered the major pollutant, while today we are aware of many others. Of these, mercury and the radioactives—primarily anti-Syphilitic remedies—probably top the bill.

However, further down the list are other suspects, the incidence of cancer in developed nations since the Second World War having increased on a steep growth curve. Epidemiologists have argued that there may be a connection between cancer and the ever-growing deployment of chemicals, particularly in agriculture and industry. A significant proportion of these chemicals is known to be carcinogenic. These include organophosphates, still commonly used as agricultural pesticides, which were first developed during the Second World War as nerve gases. After the war ended, the manufacturers sought new markets for their products. They suggested to governments, wary of continuing food shortages, that organophosphate sprays would safely protect crops from insect damage and livestock from infestation. Though the dangers of such chemicals have been known for many years, they are still widely used.

Still more inimical to life may be mixtures of different chemicals, which are rarely subjected to toxicological testing. This must lead to the advice to eat organic food and to live in an environment as free of chemicals as possible. Although maybe difficult, this is clearly of particular importance to those with young families, as eating habits are established in their earliest years—what we put before our children sets them up for life.

It is worth noting that evolution in the last fifty years has thrust us out of the Psoric garden of Eden into a predominantly Syphilitic hell. Though Carcinosin may be trimiasmatic, Sycosis and Syphilis predominate: Sycosis, because of Carcinosin's central theme of growth (more and more life in the tumour); and Syphilis, because of cancer's destructive nature (less and less life in the body).

From a psychological standpoint, the Sycotic theme translates into striving coupled with excessiveness. Because of the conflict that arises between conscience and the Sycotic's extravagant nature, they characteristically develop a deep sense of guilt and cover-up. Carcinosin symptoms which exemplify this include secretiveness and self-reproach. The Syphilitic miasm leads to the destructive expressions often exhibited by Carcinosin children, such as rudeness and defiance. Carcinosin self-destructive impulses include picking at themselves, both physically in the form of self-harming, and mentally in the form of endlessly revisiting injustices, wrongs and slights, sleeplessness, fear of cancer, and fastidiousness. These concerns and habits may be kept under wraps. It is usual for patients requiring Carcinosin, should they be fastidious, to express this as a drive for matching things. In children, and atypically, in some adults, the other polarity may be seen (predominantly Syphilitic)—smashing things up and creating mayhem.

Carcinosin children

Carcinosin children fall into two types: rebellious and conforming.

The rebellious type shows anger at reprimand, destructiveness, defiance, obstinacy and love of travel—all reminiscent of Tuberculinum. These children may be passionate and given to temper tantrums when opposed. They have strong desire natures and often exhibit early sexual interest. Both types typically have a strong reaction to rhythm and music.

The conforming type of Carcinosin, faced with heavy demands from authority figures, makes huge efforts to do well. Correct performance is deemed imperative for success. Carcinosin is one of very few remedies in the rubric, "Long history of domination by others". It is invaluable for children who cannot hold their own and are bullied at school. After bullying, they may develop physical symptoms such as a skin rash or cough. They are over-sensitive to taunts, rudeness and criticism, and take offence easily. However, these types do not become aggressive or answer back—they simply retreat and brood silently. In an attempt to fend off criticism before it is offered, they may develop perfectionism and neurotic fastidiousness. Carcinosin is well indicated in ailments of anticipation, typically sleeplessness before an event, and excessive anxiety before a performance.

Differentials

Medorrhinum and Carcinosin children typically have the same sleep position, on the knees with the face forced into the pillow. In Medorrhinum types, this facilitates sinus drainage. Carcinosin also has a position with knees drawn up to the chest, a foetal position which gives protection from big bad bullies.

Carcinosin has been successfully used to treat backwardness where the delay is due to a retreat from demands. Natrum mur types usually excel in reading and writing but are slow in speaking. This is consistent with their general reticence in communication. Baryta carb types' backwardness is usually the earliest of all to manifest. Their fear that everybody points and laughs at them because they are stupid is a secondary response to their backwardness.

The Magnesium group of remedies have points in common with Carcinosin, with their desire to be of service, suppression of aggression and shouldering of duties—too yielding and too nice for their own good. In Magnesium types, the compensation is usually relegated to their dream world, where violence may emerge.

Like Lac humanum types, many Carcinosin adults have an unresolved question in their psyche: "Am I for myself—not conforming—or am I for other people—conforming?" Carcinosin is primarily about the price you pay for conformity—being squashed. Lac humanum is about the price you pay for individuality—isolation and alienation.* This picture of Lac humanum represents such a generalised conflict for so many that in order for it to be a prescribing feature, it must dominate every aspect of the case.

Carcinosin and Aurum types both desire to please others and aspire to high values: they push themselves. Carcinosin types tend to base their standards on others' expectations, while Aurum types set them for themselves. Aurum types, if they fail, may drive themselves into hypertension, cardiovascular pathology or suicide. Along the route they may feel that they have lost the affection of their friends because they did something wrong, they failed to be a good enough person, they let themselves down. Their favoured method of suicide is by dashing themselves down from a high place.

Expectations

Carcinosin types take on board expectations from outside which feel excessively heavy, binding them in duties. The feeling is that they can never be good enough. Similarly, the cancer patient is encouraged to feel that he can never conquer the disease himself, he simply has to give himself up to whatever treatment others decide he will have. He is squashed.

Desire to please yet failure to do so

Carcinosin types are famed for their sympathetic nature and strong desire to please, to keep everyone happy. Of course, this is an impossible task. Frequently there are delusions of failure and dreams of endless striving, for instance, of flunking exams, or of looking for someone and not finding them. These dreams may utterly exhaust them. This is reflected in cancer

---

* C G Jung's concept of individuation (self-realisation), in which all aspects of the self, including the disowned or 'shadow' self, are brought fully into the light of consciousness, represents a positive resolution of this question.

patients' common feeling that the task of getting better is too great for them. However, they strive on, accepting hideous treatments to stay alive for the sake of loved ones. Carcinosin types may have dreams of having to count every grain of sand on a beach or sitting an endless run of examinations.

Symmetry

At a societal level, the polarity of conformity and rebellion as exemplified by Carcinosin is fundamental to our ability to survive. Aspects of this predate the evolution of humans. In the animal kingdom, where it is vital for survival that prey and predator recognise one another, the method of recognition is analogous to the principle of conformity and rebellion. This is the principle of symmetry and asymmetry. A predator notes its prey, and the prey notes the predator, by the break in symmetry caused by the presence of an unexpected element in the environment.

The immune system is on the lookout for an invading organism, something that does not belong (asymmetry). It fails to notice cancer cells because they are too similar to normal cells (symmetry). In health, cancer cells are created and eliminated continuously in an interplay between the forces of creation and destruction. The analogy between predator and prey becomes clear. In a healthy ecology as in a healthy body, a balance is kept between the numbers of predators and prey, and between cancerous and non-cancerous cells.

Symmetry evokes a sense of security, while asymmetry excites us because it is unexpected, perhaps even dangerous—like the relationship between predator and prey.

Art, music and symmetry

Carcinosin types are famed for their love of music and dancing. On one hand, creative nature (asymmetry) is expressed in the changing flow of the dance movements, the melodic lines, while on the other hand, symmetry is expressed in rhythm.

Carcinosin and Tuberculinum types are famed for their artistic talents. Art involves a dynamic interplay between symmetry, the known and safe element, and asymmetry, the dangerous element. Carcinosin typically expresses the symmetry pole. Carcinosin types usually enjoy more familiar forms through which to express themselves: traditional art woos us with a pleasant sense of security. Tuberculinum types more typically express the rebellious or asymmetrical pole. They enjoy the challenge of breaking the mould and creating a new form, such as revolutionary art.

Carcinosin types have a keen sense of harmony, repetition, and pattern. If they are of the conforming type, they like everything to match and coordinate, as we may notice in their clothing or interior décor. Fastidiousness is a well-known characteristic which is, however, not as neurotically predominant as it would be in the Arsenicum individual.

Carcinosin is sensitive to the beauty of nature and loves animals. This can be viewed in two lights: firstly, animals are unconditionally loving in a way that Carcinosin's demanding parents or teachers may not have been; secondly, this type's unified view of nature is reminiscent of the internal ecology operating harmoniously, exemplifying the principle of symmetry.

Nature

Like Natrum mur types, Carcinosin types are either better or worse for being at the seashore. Natrum mur types feel aggravated by the sea because they have a surfeit of dammed-up emotions. The oceans represent the emotional realm within us. For the same reason, they dislike consolation from another, because it adds to their stored emotion and makes it overflow in a way that may overwhelm and embarrass them. Natrum mur types might be ameliorated by a day visit to the sea, provided they could discharge some feelings in safety, whereas a prolonged stay in a beach bungalow may be too much of a good thing. Water added to water equals a flood. Tears tend not to ameliorate but to exhaust and weaken. When it comes to crying, they are damned if they do, and dammed if they don't!

Carcinosin's dream-come-true is a turbulent, storm-beaten sea, because it breaks the rule of symmetry. For similar reasons, they may feel strongly moved by highly emotional music and exhilarated during thunderstorms—they love to see strong emotion and turbulence expressed (asymmetry and danger).

Sepia, being burdened by duties like Carcinosin, may enjoy and be ameliorated by turbulent seas and thunderstorms because they awaken the stagnant blood!

Medorrhinum (gonorrhoea nosode) also has amelioration for being by the seashore, but usually likes to drift off in imagination by a calm sea, because of the contrast with the turbulence within. A wild sea plus a wild mind equals overload. The disorder of the mind may be expressed in unruly emotions, murderous anger, and a chaotic memory. He wants to do his own egotistical thing, to sail away, to have a prostitute in every port— gonorrhoea is common among sailors and in seaports. Physically, gonorrhoea (though nowadays suppressed) expresses in a copious discharge, whose flow becomes less sticky and purulent by the sea.

PART III

AIDS

CHAPTER 19

AIDS—THE DISEASE AND THE MIASM

It is generally thought that the disease AIDS is primarily transmitted through sex, with secondary routes of intravenous drug use and blood transfusions. AIDS results in a failure of the immune system, our last line of defence against morbific influences. The skin, the mucous membranes and organs such as the liver and gut act as a physical barrier, but when they are breached, the immune system is the final dynamic boundary. When it fails, the results are catastrophic. The breaching, or rather the failure of barriers and boundaries is the central theme of the AIDS nosode and indeed of the whole miasm.

Sex is about as close as our physical and emotional experience can get to dissolving the boundary that separates us from others, because penetration is a voluntary or involuntary breach of our personal boundary. By definition, other venereal diseases like gonorrhoea and syphilis spread through sexual intercourse, and like AIDS, thrive in situations of sex with multiple partners. However, AIDS is unlike these other diseases in that it breaches the integrity of centre of the cell, the nucleus. Thus it is by far the most difficult to treat.

If a man has what he wants, or for societal or religious reasons suppresses his libido, he does not go looking for sex elsewhere. If a man is chronically dissatisfied because he is looking for something that he cannot have, and, in an attempt to plug the hunger gap, tries to find it with multiple sexual partners, venereal organisms have a field day. The question is, what is the gap he is trying to plug?

Love, sex, and power

Everyone wants to experience unconditional love in a simple and open way, but the world is deficient in this commodity. Our Psoric need drives us to desire love and sex (suppression of libido is the purely Psoric expression) and our Sycotic instability leads us to seek love and sex outside of one relationship.

While gay lifestyles are becoming increasingly accepted, many gays still feel sidelined and outcast. This builds upon Psora, adding a Syphilitic descant of aversion. Love becomes doubly conditional because not only is it contingent upon fulfilling expectations within your immediate group, but you and your friends are ostracised. This is the psychological and spiritual platform on which the AIDS miasm is mounted: the Syphilitic elements of feeling outcast, dirty, and contaminated; and the Psoric element of separation from the source of love.

Heterosexuals are not ostracised, but they have the same needs, and certain societies have allowed for promiscuity. In some African countries whose men have multiple sexual partners, whole tribes are being wiped out by AIDS.

If it is the mark of your manhood to have many, you have given up on love in favour of power. The man with the power to attract many women is the envy of other men: his standing is represented by his harem. As we all know, power and love are a pair of opposites. An absence of love (Psoric) in part drives AIDS, but a love of power (Syphilitic) may place the disease in tribal Africa as well as in gay communities. A gay man is commonly referred to as a queen, denoting superior status as well as sardonically commenting on his mannerisms. A queen is the most powerful and elevated member of society.

From the homeopathic point of view, it is hard to resist the association of queens with Platina. Platina has bold type rubrics like "love of her own sex". Also the remedy lies upon an axis of distancing self from others by becoming taller and better than them, versus isolation feelings; of sexual power versus degradation and dirtiness (*Complete Repertory* has 20 rubrics referring to dirtiness).

AIDS and the miasms

From the point of view of miasmatic analysis, Tuberculosis and AIDS are similar. AIDS patients commonly succumb to tuberculosis. Certainly both diseases are associated with youthful deaths—it is not unusual for our talented rebels, writers and musicians, to be whisked away in the full bloom of their creative output. Both diseases represent a marriage of Psora and Syphilis. In the case of tuberculosis, the homeland (Psora) has been destroyed (Syphilis). In the case of AIDS, the destruction (Syphilis) is of the personal boundary (Psora).

The story of AIDS and its discovery is bound up with the gay communities in San Francisco and Manhattan. Here, casual sex with multiple partners had been the rule. This is an attempt at an impossible union, too much thinning of the boundary. As well as providing a pathway of infection, this lifestyle has resulted in frequent venereal infections and associated allopathic treatments, which tend to weaken the immune system. A hunger for intimacy expressing in 'perverted' form in superficial unions may be associated with low self-esteem (and its compensation of arrogance) and feelings of isolation. Witness the gay community and its still common exclusion from most heterosexual society. Gay stands for "Good as you!" With the arrival of AIDS-related symptoms, a pervading sense of desperation and destruction entered the picture—the Syphilitic note.

Gays who have multiple partners are more at risk of exposure to venereal disease and hepatitis and resulting allopathic drug treatments. Gays are also more likely than other groups to use recreational drugs such as amyl nitrate, which heightens sexual orgasm. Such assaults severely compromise the immune system, which in turn predisposes them to AIDS. Anal sex too provides an easy route for infections to invade, as the thin membrane of the rectum is easily torn.

In Africa, additional causes of under-functioning immune systems may be malnutrition and poverty. Currently, Africa is experiencing a series of wars, which lead to dispossession (Tubercular miasm) and the ripping apart of tribal and family boundaries (AIDS miasm).

AIDS—an introduction to the disease

The organisms which cause opportunistic infections in AIDS patients are present in humans all of the time, the difference being that healthy immune systems do not provide an 'opening' for their proliferation. Infections common in the latter stages include candida albicans, herpes simplex, herpes varicella zoster, cytomegalovirus, pneumocystis carinii, cryptococcus, toxoplasmosis, cryptosporidiosis, histoplasmosis and salmonella. It is noticeable that with the exception of salmonella—a virulent bacteria which causes severe gastro-enteritis—the organisms are parasites and fungi. In Stage 5 (Ward Reed Classification System) fungal infections of the mouth, vagina, anus and skin are common; in Stage 6, inroads occur at a much deeper level including lungs, brain, liver and bone marrow. Another condition commonly found in a virulent form as an AIDS-related complex is Kaposi's Sarcoma, normally a rather benign skin malignancy characterised by purple lesions.

In simple terms, the body's defence system becomes susceptible to infiltration by the alien organism (HIV) which acts to shut down the mechanisms maintaining the balance between the inner and outer world. The immune system ceases, over time, to work on behalf of the whole. The organisms which are normally present in humans cease to be held in check and states of chronic infection become the rule rather than the exception.

The mechanism of the Human Immunodeficiency Virus

In the early 1980s, researchers in France and America found a retrovirus that was later called HIV (Human Immunodeficiency Virus), which was associated with AIDS. Retroviruses infiltrate the cell and subvert its genetic mechanism to procreate themselves.

RNA is usually a messenger molecule that transfers the genetic code from the DNA in the cell nucleus to the ribosomes where proteins are built up according to the DNA blueprint. HIV contains small pieces of RNA which work in reverse: they alter the DNA.

This raises an important point about how miasms evolve. If we accept the model of miasms developing over the centuries as diseases become more suppressed and go deeper into the organism (with Psora being the simplest and earliest, and Cancer and AIDS being the most complex and 'civilised'), we can appreciate that AIDS affects the most fundamental level of life, the genetic structure itself.

In HIV infection, the virus enters T4 cells in the blood. Once inside the cell the virus releases an enzyme, reverse transcriptase, which causes small pieces of RNA in the virus to produce a relatively short length of DNA. This piece of DNA becomes part of the infected cell's genome and starts producing RNA, which will in turn become part of a new virus. In this process the host T4 cell, a leukocyte which has an important role in the working of the immune system, is destroyed and the whole system is compromised.

Not everyone is convinced that HIV is the real cause of AIDS. Harris Coulter is one of many who have questioned the link. Those most likely to get the disease are also those with broken-down immune systems, either through conditions such as haemophilia, or through the abuse of drugs and a history of allopathically treated venereal disease. The issue of whether HIV causes AIDS has become impossible to analyse as the presence of antibodies to HIV has now become the definition of AIDS. Thus patients with HIV antibodies dying of pneumonia are classified as a dying of AIDS, while those without the antibodies are classified as a dying of pneumonia. Note that this debate does not affect the integrity of the homeopathic AIDS nosode as it was made not from an isolated virus but from the blood of a man who died of AIDS.

A brief history of the disease

The first AIDS cases appeared in Manhattan and San Francisco in the US. In 1981 a few unexplained cases of Pneumicystis carinii pneumonia (PCP) appeared in apparently healthy young men in metropolitan areas of the USA. PCP is a rare form of parasitic pneumonia that previously had only been seen in the very old and very young or in those with compromised immune systems—usually through malnutrition or immuno-suppressant drugs.

Doctors were also reporting an increase in the number of cases of Kaposi's sarcoma, a rare form of skin cancer that had also only been known in people with weakened immune systems. Again, this condition was appearing in fit young men. The only connecting factor between these patients was that they were almost exclusively gay and predominantly promiscuously gay.

The appearance of opportunistic infections in apparently healthy young men was called Gay Related Immune Deficiency, GRID. By the end of 1983 there had been more than 2,500 cases in the USA and all over the developed world.

By this time it was clear that the disease was not restricted to gay men. It was also appearing in haemophiliacs, intravenous drug users and the female partners of bisexual men. The disease was renamed Acquired Immune Deficiency Syndrome, AIDS.

The appearance of AIDS in haemophiliacs and intravenous drug users was taken to indicate that it was an infectious disease and that the infectious agent was carried in the blood. The appearance of AIDS in the female partners of high-risk men indicated that the infectious agent was probably present also in semen. The cases of babies suggested that breast milk might also be a carrier. The obvious conclusion was that all bodily fluids, including saliva, were possible carriers of the infectious agent. What had at first seemed to be restricted to a particular and somewhat isolated community now came to be seen as a plague that could affect everyone. It appeared that even a simple kiss could be a death sentence.

This view was confirmed by the African experience. At the same time that AIDS was appearing in the USA and the developed world, a strange new disease was appearing in parts of Africa. This disease caused wasting, hence it came to be called 'Slim', and it opened up the affected person to opportunistic infections from which he or she usually died. In Africa 'Slim' was, and still is, killing an enormous number of men and women who should be in the prime of their lives. In Africa, AIDS is clearly a heterosexual disease.

AIDS and drug abuse have been closely linked since the first appearance of the disease. Intravenous heroin users are particularly susceptible. In a number of cities the problems of heroin addiction and HIV have almost merged into one. The isolation, secrecy and numbness of the heroin state, seen as the only way out of unbearable pain, echo important issues in the AIDS state. In the 1980s and 1990s, AIDS patients tended to be viewed as despicable and unclean; they were shunned in much the same way as junkies. If you are viewed as despicable and unclean, you isolate yourself and develop habits of secrecy. An example of a nation acting in this way is Burma, whose primary trade is in heroin. It is claimed that 50% of its men are addicted to heroin and are suffering from AIDS. Thus the blood money of heroin is AIDS. This brings into sharp focus the Syphilitic aspect of the AIDS state.

When news of AIDS first sprang upon the world, most were deeply shocked. Fear of death and moral indignation combined to create a gloomy and apocalyptic prognosis of the future. It seemed as if a new plague was to be let loose upon the world. In an effort to control what was threatening to become a devastating epidemic, governments launched massive advertising campaigns to encourage 'safe sex'. Images of gravestones engraved with the word 'AIDS' were shown in TV commercials urging people to us condoms.

By the late 1990s, much of the terror and hype about AIDS had died away. In the developed world at least, the disease is common only in certain quite restricted and well-defined groups. The plague has not come to suburbia, as many feared it would. Even for those with the disease, a cocktail of powerful drugs is significantly extending life expectancy. Despite this sobering of our view of AIDS, our initial collective response is held as a memory within the 'genius' of the nosode.

Even among those who concur that HIV causes AIDS, dispute has arisen as to where the virus came from. In his book *Emerging Viruses: AIDS & Ebola: Nature, Accident or Intentional?** Leonard Horowitz collates evidence which suggests that HIV did not naturally evolve and spontaneously jump species from African monkeys to man, as one well-argued view claims. Horowitz maintains that HIV was genetically engineered from existing animal and human viruses, with government involvement, for bio-warfare and defence purposes. The new virus then made its way by cross-contamination into hepatitis, polio and smallpox vaccines manufactured by the same companies. This cross-contamination theory is supported by the fact that the locations and dates at which the vaccines were first trialled in the US and Africa were the same as those where AIDS was first identified. In both countries, the first AIDS cases were noted just three months after the beginning of the vaccine trials.

At this time in the US, homosexual men and intravenous drug users were noted to be at high risk of contracting hepatitis and were targeted by the government and drug companies for new hepatitis vaccinations. In Africa, smallpox and polio vaccinations were promoted in addition to hepatitis.

---

* Sandpoint, Idaho: Tetrahedron, 1996

Horowiz's theory, shared by some scientists involved in AIDS research, underlies the mistrust with which certain groups, including some African populations and gay organisations in the US, view orthodox Western medical intervention in their AIDS cases.

While we make no judgement as to the truth of the theory, it has an important bearing on two AIDS nosode themes: betrayal, and the breaking down of the boundaries that constitute our immune system.

The second theme, breaking down of boundaries, has special relevance to the process of genetic engineering. Genetic engineering involves inserting pieces of genetic material or DNA from one organism into the genome of another organism. Often this is done across species or even across kingdoms—for example, genes from a spider or fish are inserted into the genome of a crop plant to confer some desired trait such as frost resistance or toxicity to insect pests.

The breaking of natural boundaries between species and kingdoms sets genetic engineering apart from all traditional breeding techniques and gives rise to its controversial nature and inherent riskiness. In traditional techniques, cross-breeding can only be carried out between closely related organisms with a very similar genetic makeup, such as a horse and a donkey (producing a mule), or a tangerine and a grapefruit (producing a tangelo). You cannot cross a horse with a dog, or a grapefruit with a bacterium or virus. Nature sets up strong boundaries between different organisms that make it near impossible for foreign genetic material to invade an organism's genome. These boundaries explain why people seldom fall victim to plant or animal viruses and why horses do not take on the qualities of the grass they eat every day.

But with genetic engineering, these natural boundaries are bypassed. The method of getting the foreign gene construct into the host organism's genome is revolutionary and violent. Because cell walls are resistant to invasion, the process has been likened to breaking into a reinforced concrete bunker. The gene constructs are introduced directly into plant cells by physical methods that damage cells, such as a gun that shoots in gold particles coated with the genetic material or, in the case of animal cells, a strong electric field that creates holes in the cell membrane. Another method involves splicing the constructs into artificial vectors, made up of bits of different viruses, mobile genetic elements called transposons, and plasmids, pieces of genetic material that replicate independently of the chromosome in bacteria, yeasts and other cells. While natural viruses, transposons and plasmids are generally restricted in their movements by genetic barriers between species, genetically engineered vectors and gene constructs are designed to cross all species barriers and to overcome normal mechanisms that breakdown, inactivate or inhibit foreign DNA. They may therefore be more likely to move between species and bypass the immune system.*

The problem with the genetic engineering process is that it disrupts the host genome in an imprecise and unpredictable way. Scientists cannot know where the inserted genetic material will end up, how it will express in the new host, and how it will mutate in the future. Some have warned that such disruption to the host's genome, and the use of viral vectors and promoters, are likely to result in genetic mutations, cancer of the organism or virulent new superviruses.

In the case of HIV, Horowitz and his supporters argue that bio-warfare and/or vaccine research led to animal viruses being taught to cross species barriers, making a monkey virus suddenly become lethal to man. Certainly the appearance of AIDS coincided with the rise of genetic engineering in the late 1970s and early 1980s, and both these events coincided with a marked upsurge in scientific reports of viruses mutating and jumping species barriers.

With respect to the central dynamic of the AIDS nosode, we could say that the genetic engineering aspect of the 'AIDS mythology' links with the theme of disruption of the organism's boundaries at the most profound level—that of the DNA.

Our knowledge of the effects of genetic engineering is still in its infancy, though products of the technique are now present in a high proportion of processed foods. What little research has been conducted indicates that problems may arise in those who consume such foods, including

---

* Our thanks are due to Dr Mae-Wan Ho for explaining the genetic engineering process in her book *Living with the Fluid Genome* (2003), available from http://www.i-sis.org.uk/fluidGenome.php

abnormal immune response, cell proliferation and unexplained infections of the vital organs.

Observations about AIDS patients

Some of the traits and behaviours seen in AIDS patients may also be seen in homeopathic patients needing the AIDS nosode. We have included in brackets symptoms from the proving where relevant:

- Surrendering to standard medical interventions or developing monomaniacal approaches to learning all about the disease. This reminds us of Carcinosin.
- Feeling that the health care giver is a partner ("feelings of empathy", "desire to share honestly and with feeling")—they must explain every move to the satisfaction of the patient or they will be distrusted and may be dismissed ("suspicion", "nobody loves me", "felt lied to", "felt rejected", "felt betrayed").
- Fear of exposure and feeling unacceptable ("suspicion", "fears that people are plotting against them or talking about them", "desire to be naked").
- A feeling of peace and calm, surrender to a higher power—in contrast to the state of mind present when contracting the illness ("tranquillity", "serenity", "calmness").
- Because the illness is almost always kept secret until some great force precipitates its revelation, the patient has low self-esteem, often masked with a thick veneer of bravado and self-importance. Once the patient 'comes out', a great relief is felt and another stage is set. This stage can be a breakthrough into acceptance and forgiveness— also by loved ones and family.
- Gay anal sex touches on three fundamental taboos: sex, shit and homosexuality ("delusions, they have done wrong", "delusions, everything they said was wrong").
- Self-destructive state, exemplified by numerous sexual partners ("dreams, having sex with several people"), sexually transmitted diseases (cutting pains in the penis and pain during and after urination, reminiscent of the symptoms of gonorrhoea), recreational drugs and prescribed drugs for venereal and other diseases, including antibiotics, sulphanilamides, steroids and antifungals.

CHAPTER 20

THE PROVING OF THE AIDS NOSODE*—
BREAKDOWN OF BOUNDARIES

A Syphilo-Psoric (AIDS miasm) nosode

The first proving of the AIDS nosode was undertaken in 1988 using single doses in either the 30th or 200th centesimal potencies of the blood of a man who subsequently died of AIDS-related diseases. Results of the initial proving, though portraying some symptom patterns, did not convey the 'shape' of the remedy. Therefore, some pillules were sent to Mariette Honig in Holland who carried out a similarly exhaustive proving. The verified symptoms of these provings have been included in the extraction presented. However, the picture of the nosode emerged with flying colours when in 1994 we carried out two group provings with students at The School of Homeopathy. One group received 30c and the other 200c.

At the School we have carried out all our provings with unit doses. This stimulus, because it is amplified by the group and reawakened at monthly gatherings when experiences are recounted, is sufficient to produce significant and long-range effects.

During the course of the School weekend (Friday through to Sunday) we took stock of thoughts, dreams, sensations, feelings and external world events, using transcripts of tape recordings to ensure accuracy, and diaries kept by supervisors and provers. Audio recording spanned a period of three months, while some reports of cured symptoms continued to come in for the next two years.

---

* For the full proving text and Repertory of the AIDS nosode proving, please visit the School of Homeopathy website at www.homeopathyschool.com and link through to the provings section. Information is also available on the databases of MacRepertory, RADAR, CARA and ISIS.

THE PROVING OF THE AIDS NOSODE

Major themes in the proving

Because the AIDS nosode is a relatively new remedy, insufficient clinical evidence exists as to the 'AIDS type' of patient. However, some consistent themes emerged, many with strong motifs of boundaries (houses, walls, rooms, shell, contamination, popping seeds and bubbles), rejection, and isolation:

- Content. Serene. Relaxed. Confident. Elated.
- Sensation of things coming out; of flying gently, of floating, of being uplifted; of love and companionship for everyone; of growth, of blossoming.
- Playful. Remembered childhood.
- Expansive. Extravagant.
- Wanton. Invulnerable. Reckless.
- Sympathetic. Sensitive.
- Massive. Passive. Slow. Can't be bothered. Dull.
- Fragile. Weak. Exposed. Shy. Dependent. Panic. Can't cope.
- Confused. Forgetful. Making mistakes. Concentration difficult.
- Restless. Frustrated. Irritable. Easily offended. Insensitive. Violent. Desire to kill.
- Feeling rejected; "... does not belong"; "... felt excluded, lied to"; outcast.
- Feeling betrayed. Suspicious. Persecuted.
- Withdrawn. Wants to be alone. Isolated.
- Frightened. Loss of identity.
- Loss of protection/shell/wall. "I felt that I had lost my wall and my shell, and there was a free flow of emotions both in and out. I was exposed, almost naked, with no control." "... uninterrupted flow between self and group".
- Feeling contaminated and fear of contaminating others (always washing).
- Self-loathing.
- Responsibility for others; responsibility for children.
- Left-sidedness.

Curative response to the remedy proving

I think the curative action of the proving [of the AIDS nosode] is that I did have a sense of feeling that I belonged with people that I had never had before. I had always felt like I was outside and unacceptable, so all the while, whilst I might look like I was part of the group, I actually felt myself on the outside.

The night of the proving, I slept really well, like I haven't slept in ages. Very comfortably. I remember my dreams were very colourful, I remember a whole load of flowers. [a number of provers in the initial stages of the proving reported images of flowers and seeds.] Usually my dreams are very unlike that, basically very dark, very violent, as if there is something following me, there is blackness and I don't know what is going on. Constant nightmares rather than dreams. The nightmares have completely stopped. And one more thing that has stopped is that I no longer always feel crushed, like there is a heavy weight and as if I am being sexually tortured in some way.

And the other thing that went after the proving, is a lot of anal bleeding and vaginal pain, which I realise dates back to tearing.

I don't throw up when people hug me. It's quite an advantage actually, it's kind of detrimental to relationships! But yes, I used to be very nauseous around touch and my osteopath really noticed it, that she was able to work on me much more. Before I would have a delayed reaction to the session. Over time we had found a way of working but I would still vomit afterwards, maybe even a day later.

I feel a bit like a small child. I think before, I felt that there was this small child in this adult's body, screaming its head off to be heard. That was one of the things I felt I carried, this giant scream around in me all the time. I don't have that now. I guess it's the difference between vulnerable and open. I feel like a more open small child who will be able to receive and take things; whereas before, I just felt completely vulnerable, and terrified, making sure that I kept people out, and yet desperately wanting to be in contact with them as well.

Dream themes

For the provers of the AIDS nosode the most striking and reoccurring image to appear, particularly in dreams, was the form of a house. More than half of the dreamers had this. This image was reiterated in many different configurations and can be used to describe the wider picture of the remedy. We will offer interpretations of this imagery when we come to it towards the end of the proving. Dream themes included:

- Huge houses, vast rooms, small outside, huge within;
- Houses or things richly ornate, jewelled, gold, beautiful interiors, colours stunning and rich;
- Big, grand houses, ornate, ramshackle or both;
- Staircases and corridors;
- Wood, metal, water;
- Colour: red;
- Violence;
- Panic;
- Responsibility;
- Anger, irritability;
- Fear;
- Teeth;
- Snow;
- Septic state;
- Children;
- Transport, travelling, buses, cars, trains, airports, bus station, train station;
- Lots of people/being busy/rushing about.

The 'story' of the AIDS nosode*

To recapitulate: the pathological action of HIV is to bring about a failure of the immune system, our last line of defence against morbific influences. The skin, mucous membranes and organs such as the gut and

---

* This arrangement and selection of symptoms from the full proving has been compiled by Peter Fraser, author of *The AIDS Miasm: Contemporary Disease and the New Remedies,* The Winter Press.

liver act as a physical barrier, but when they are breached the immune system is the final, dynamic barrier and when it fails, the results are catastrophic. The failure of barriers and boundaries is the central theme of the AIDS nosode and indeed of the whole miasm.

The feeling of having no boundaries between oneself and the world, of being vulnerable, naked and exposed is therefore perhaps the most basic feeling of the nosode.

> *I felt that I had lost my wall, my protection and my shell, there was a free flow of emotions both in and out. I was exposed, almost naked, with no control.*

> *... uninterrupted flow between self and group...*

> *I am being over-sensitive: exceptionally sympathetic to the point of tears—weepy. Things are getting to me, usually I couldn't give a damn—I am feeling very fragile.*

The shell is the image or metaphor that most clearly and straightforwardly expresses the barrier and the feeling of being without it.

> *Felt very exposed—I had no shell to protect me.*

In homeopathy the remedy and the disease are similar. The remedy does what the disease was trying to do, but not quite succeeding in doing. The disease must therefore contain not only the actual hell of illness but a glimpse of the heaven that will heal. The most valuable symptoms of a patient and the most indicative proving symptoms will be ones in which this contradiction is strong. The AIDS nosode symptom in which this is most powerfully expressed is:

> *Exquisite and precious mental pain—I had no shell for protection.*

The lack of a protective shell is truly painful but that pain is exquisite and precious because it allows the possibility of connecting with people and the world and offers a release from isolation.

A similar sense of escaping the things that separate us from the world is found in a desire to be naked or natural:

I wanted to do something wanton and sensual and extravagant, last night. I felt frustrated—I wanted to swim naked in the sea or ride a horse naked or something naked.

I felt like doing something mischievous. I wanted to do something naked and extravagant. I had no embarrassment with nakedness.

I felt like I had to keep my feet on the ground, the only way to describe it would be as a delusion really—a tribal one; Cheyenne with tepees and people and it was pleasant and the sensation was very, very real to me.

Everything felt natural, tribal—like the south sea islands, natural barefoot, nothing much underneath, with flowers, natural, with white, green and water.

There was a similar desire to be emotionally naked and avoid the things that create barriers between us and the world. Again, the vulnerability that is the disease and the possibility of connection that is the healing are almost one and the same thing.

Decided to simplify my life by not encumbering it with charitable obligations.

Feelings of empathy. Desire to share honestly and with feeling.

A lack of insulation between the self and the world leads to an over-sensitivity that in turn leads to restlessness and irritability.

Feel continuously restless inside.

Great feelings of anger and impatience, triggered by having to wait one and a half hours for an appointment.

Make lots of mistakes on the computer today, and got bloody irritable about it!

For some reason I am really irritable today, mostly at inanimate objects: the car, packaging on biscuits, the computer and so on. Glad to get into bed at the end of the day without smashing something.

Later that day found I was getting very irritated by the clients at work, I did not want to be there doing that job. Went home and was irritable with husband. Why?

The reaction to this is to detach from the world. Detachment is often expressed as a sense of floating or flying or manifests as vertigo:

I feel much calmer. When I arrived I was quite upset because I had just been told that a friend had died. I am concerned, but not in a way that feels overwhelming.

By the afternoon I felt above it all, serene, even rested... was able to listen to landlord being racist and let it pass over my head instead of getting worked up.

I feel above it all, I feel that I am floating, I feel disconnected, I felt I had to ground myself, the world seems an exciting and strange place.

Dreamt of flying. I was in the New Zealand mountains soaring and playing above the snow, swooping—very white. Sky was very blue. I was playing, being reckless and it was such an amazing feeling. I was on a hang glider, one hand, being reckless, but such a feeling, incredible.

Dreams of being in outer space.

A slight dizzy feeling going upwards, uplifting really.

Sensation of flying gently, of floating, of being uplifted.

Another manifestation of detachment is a feeling of numbness:

Numbness of fingers and toes on waking.

There is in the remedy a sense of isolation.

Want to get away from everyone. Yet when on my own want to be with everyone again.

Felt very withdrawn.

Not connecting with people—feelings of isolation—felt, 'nobody loves me'.

First evening alone for a long time and I don't like it.

Really clingy.

Had the desire to be alone. Felt different to and separate from other people. Felt very individual.

I suddenly felt, "I don't belong here at all".

There is a sense of connection or a desire to connect in many ways: with family, friends, and partner, but also with nature and the divine.

I noticed last night that I was in and out of the room doing what I wanted to do and being part of the group as well.

Good connection with wife; talked about finding wholeness in the midst of feelings of separation and diversity. The need for spiritual wholeness is great. Synergy: through pursuing creative, enjoyable and relaxing spiritual pursuits together!

Felt very connected to family and friends.

This is a big deal for me—it feels as though barriers between me and other people can come down with this man. (Talking about new relationship.)

Sensation of love and companionship for everyone.

Peacefulness, mildness. A feeling of complete peace of mind. A feeling of oneness with my fellow man and the whole of the universe. I felt exceptionally close to my family and friends. All I could think of was: youth, beauty, peace.

Everything in life works more perfectly. There is a new order in things.

Pathologically this is more likely to be found in a sense of disconnection.

Feelings of being awkward and shy—averse company and talking.

Absence of sensitivity towards others.

Estrangement.

Given that HIV is a venereal disease it is not surprising that in the nosode this was strongly manifested in sexual feelings.

Dreamt I was about to embark on an affair with a married, middle aged businessman, just for the sex. We didn't do it though because the night passed in carousing with friends.

Decided to separate from partner in the last two days.

Felt distant from my wife. Feelings of abandonment and lack of love. Feel there is not enough time for closeness and intimacy.

Disinterested in sex and do not have my customary morning erection.

Sex drive very low, really can't be bothered.

Libido is not there. Don't seem to fancy husband sexually.

At its most extreme it becomes a feeling of paranoia, that everyone is against them.

The first thing I noticed after taking the remedy was that beforehand I had been very sociable and after taking the remedy I started to feel very self-conscious and kind of almost paranoid and I went and sat in the corner.

At the weekend I kept missing people, not connecting. Felt people were picking on me, felt isolated.

Felt that people were plotting against me.

Felt very strong fear of heights when visiting the cliffs. Lay down and looked over the edge, even while lying down felt great terror (much more than usual) and a mistrust of people behind me, as if they might push me over the edge. (Unusual.)

Oversensitive really. Things are going wrong. Normally I take them in my stride. Been pathetic. What's the matter with me? Suspicious. Nobody loves me. Not normally like this.

Felt lied to, angry, frustrated.

Feeling rejected; outcast.

Feeling betrayed.

I had the feeling of being picked on. I got really close to people as if I could see them really clearly, and I wanted to meet them in the group. And the feeling I had was that no one would come to meet me and I felt very closed and unhappy. I felt this frustration that no one was coming to play.

Felt people did not like me. With people but had feeling they did not like me. Sitting there and not wanting to be sociable. Feeling they don't like me. Not like me at all.

Felt that people were plotting against me.

This tends to be turned back on to the self with feelings of shame and lack of self-worth.

I imagined everything I said was wrong—that I had offended someone—that I had committed some sort of faux pas.

Feeling that people are looking at me and saying "she's no good".

Self-loathing.

An inability to connect clearly with the outside world leads to a feeling of confusion and forgetfulness.

Feeling of "cotton wool" in the head, slight vertigo. Difficulty concentrating.

I was really conscious all night about having to remember my dreams and having to disentangle whether I was in a dream, whether it was a dream, that sort of half-conscious state.

Continually sensing that I have forgotten something or forgotten to do something.

This forgetfulness is not me. I am usually very organized. Also finding I lose words. Know what I want to say but the odd word just vanishes.

Mind going completely blank.

Forgetfulness. Forgot to put on clean pants. Put my top on back to front. Realized that I had put my trousers on back to front as well.

Loss of words, cannot express himself.

This lack of clarity would seem also to apply to the symptoms of the nosode which are often of a low grade undifferentiated type.

One of the features of HIV and of the AIDS nosode is an issue around secrets and openness. People living with HIV are often very secretive about their status but at the same time can be immensely open about their lives and suffering. Again this clear contradiction indicates it is an important issue in the disease and the nosode.

The remedy's secrecy meant that its nature was not immediately revealed. Fortunately, those involved in the group proving (where they felt safe and 'held') recognised this and persevered.

Many of the provers in all the provings experienced dreams of houses and particularly of large and ornate buildings. Not only were these dreams common but they were the things that most struck people about the proving. The combination of being so common and so striking indicates that such dreams are almost certainly a keynote of the remedy.

The house is a complex image and metaphor that contains within it most of the major issues of the AIDS nosode.

Just as for the mollusc, the snail or the hermit crab their shell is their house, so for us the house is our shell with all that that entails. The house is our protection against the weather and all that might threaten our safety from without. Provers had a number of dreams in which safety inside the house was threatened by danger outside.

I dreamed of a Georgian terrace on a high pavement. I had a smaller apartment within this large house. I remember there were lots of weird things going on with drug dealers, threats and violence. I had big, strong male friends and I took them up there to protect me but the drug dealers had gone.

There was a magic golden key which could unlock or lock any door. Immediately it came in handy because suddenly the boy realized there was a madman outside the door with a knife. It was as if the boy could see through the door. The madman was standing at the door with the knife raised, and so the boy quickly locked the door so that he couldn't come in.

I went to a party where the place got smashed up. Someone kept telling these thugs that I was a friend, but I wasn't and they were looking pretty mean as if they would start to work on me next.

I was an onlooker and there was this medieval army with a red hot battering ram attacking a castle. There were three figures of flame, just human figures which burst into flame of red and orange. It was really, really frightening.

Dreams of threats of violence.

A sense of vulnerability was found throughout the remedy.

I had to find a place to get some earrings, and a local man with a truck was taking me there. But he took me down a ramp to a car park underground, with the truck's lights off and no lighting in the car park. I knew he was going to rape me and that the car lights were off to show that he knew where he was going, he was in charge, he had all the power. I was a helpless victim, pleading with him not to do it (and at the same time wishing that I did have the opportunity to have sex with someone I love). I felt I couldn't escape.

Dream of a circular tall hole in the side of my tent and it was definitely a wolf that had done it.

Dream that a giant black dog, six feet long, four feet tall, a man-eater, was on the loose and after us, especially me.

I dreamt of a mass murder.

Dreadful dreams of fear.

Poverty and particularly dirt and disease were also very threatening.

Dream of seeing an old friend and being disturbed that he is so poor.

Dream about flies. Lots of flies' eggs mixed in with white rice in the boot of a car. I knew they would hatch out and he was waiting for it to happen. Sense of fear of the swarm of flies.

I dream that I am looking for a toilet as I need to poo. But everywhere I go there is either a very dirty toilet, or one with no lock, or one with people in the cubicles.

Dreamt that a friend told me a mutual ex-boyfriend had all along been having sex and therefore (sic) we were both at risk from HIV and AIDS.

Feeling contaminated and fear of contaminating others; always washing.

Great fear of terminal illness.

Fear of impending disease.

This vulnerability was particularly applicable to children and the childlike state.

I felt vulnerable, that I needed someone to look after me. I felt like a child, but it was a good feeling.

What I have been noticing is that I want someone else to feed me. It is very difficult for me to feed myself at the moment, as if I am a helpless infant in a cradle.

I need someone to look after me but can't bring myself to ask— too much effort.

Dreams of having to protect children were common.

It was like a community in this house but I was the only adult and there were gunmen surrounding the house and we were in danger and I felt a great sense of responsibility because I had to somehow gather all these animals and children with me and I knew what I had to do, I had to get them out but it was really difficult and felt really unwieldy because I had to get everyone together to get them to safety.

I had a dream that I was in this department store all night and I had to make sure that the whole gang of children that were with me weren't pinching things and touching things.

In one of my dreams this morning, I was in charge of a roller-coaster, and responsible for providing space for all the people who wanted a ride. I didn't have enough harnesses to hold them all in and there was this small child and a baby and I had to rig up harnesses for them. I remember watching them coming down and thinking that the harnesses didn't look very safe. I think the baby got its legs chopped off, but I don't know—I couldn't find out.

Dream of having to look after a group of children.

Concern about children, needing protection.

Another common dream theme was that of injured animals.

Dreamt I was in a car accident which ran over my dog, but when I got home he was alive, but a different colour and had a horrible septic state all over his paws and legs, which had taken the fur off, leaving raw flesh.

Dreamt I came across a nearly dead otter—lots of wounds—covered in blood.

A prover who was notably cured by the remedy gave the following story.

A few years ago he had a nervous breakdown because of financial difficulties, his brothers and sisters all ignored him and he felt very low. What finally lifted him out of his depression was the arrival of a tiny, stray kitten. "I was at home all day, moping around, and then this little kitten arrived. It kept coming up to me, purring and nudging me and suddenly I felt: I am accepted, I am part of this world again."

Dreams of childhood homes were important, as were memories of childhood in general.

In my dream my parents are moving house—I say, "this time I want the room at the top, not my old room." As a child I always wanted the room at the top of the house. I loved the

*eaves and it was by my parents' room. More importantly it
was not next door to my brother's room—it would have been
an escape from the place where he (and a gang of friends) had
abused me.*

*I am back in the house with my mum and stepfather, which
they bought when I was 14 years old. Never had a dream in
that house before, unusual.*

Journeying into the past, remembering childhood experiences.

The most colourful and striking dreams of houses were of buildings that
were grand or palatial and lavish.

*A huge, huge mansion house in the middle of a park where
you drive up to it. I was buying a smaller flat within this huge
house.*

*We went to this house. There were lots of boxes in this house
and very big rooms, but everything was decorated beautifully.
There were chandeliers, beautiful furniture, beautiful
paintings, antique carpets and there were railings and you just
looked down and there was a great feeling of space.*

*I dreamed I lived in a huge mansion with lots of beautiful
antiques and artefacts. It was stuffed full of them. It looked
encrusted. Every surface had beautiful things on it. Tables with
collections of pretty handbags on them. It was chunky, solid
furniture, but lovely. Collections of things everywhere. There
was a huge marble staircase. I remember thinking, "Oh, I do
live in a lovely place".*

*The room in my dream was big, in fact I couldn't see the walls
clearly because they were all misty.*

Often the houses had many stairs.

Dreamt of a house with banisters and lots of stairs.

The stairs were very large in the house in my dream.

The word that was most commonly used to describe this lavishness was
"ornate".

Walking upstairs in House of Commons through enormous rooms, grand, ornate decor—out of another time.

In a Catholic church, very rich gold paintings, colours, statues.

The house is an image of the material. "Bricks and mortar" is a term used to describe the ultimate in solid and enduring wealth.

There could be in the remedy a sense of mass and passivity.

I had a very strong image of an elephant and the feeling was a gentleness and a passivity but also this enormous physical structure.

Feel well, although I do seem much slower than my usual pace.

Even before this proving, where so many people dreamt of houses, I had often said to myself: "The foundations aren't right". Now I feel the foundations have been put in order.

The theme of materialism is also found in the remedy's strong treasure imagery.

The treasure was shown to me earlier in the dream—a medieval knight with a thick gold, very old, very beautiful wedding ring, that is just a part... there is more to be found.

They brought in these crates and opened them up. The crates had false centres that were packed full of treasure. There was gold dripping out and jewels and crowns. They were full of treasures and I was really excited.

The father gave the boy some magical gifts from the mother and these were very special significant things. The first thing was a sword in a jewelled holder and they hid it under the bed so that no one else would see because it was a special magic sword. Then there were magic blue boxing gloves with which the boy could knock anyone out. There was also a bejewelled brooch—and that was significant but I didn't know why. Then there was a magic golden key which could unlock or lock any door.

Treasure is a wonderful thing and can be a metaphor for all that is beautiful and desirable. But treasure, like all material things, is of Hades realm rather than the realm of life. Gems and precious metals are dug from deep in the earth and, in time, return to it. The archetypal treasure is the buried kind.

> *My wonderful room leads out to the garden which is a mass of dark brown earth. My father says I have only this one day to dig for the treasure because tomorrow he has arranged to have it planted up and laid over.*

Treasure often turns out to be false or not of real value.

> *I am mining in a desert country for rock crystals. I find only amethysts, which is a nuisance because I am looking for diamonds.*

> *I was travelling with people in a car, and when we got there I realized it was my parents' house. A lot of money had been spent on it in a garish way and I didn't like it.*

In many religions and symbologies a concern with the material world is associated with death—and death is undoubtedly a major theme in the AIDS nosode. The appearance of AIDS, an unknown disease that could strike anywhere and which was inexorably and inevitably fatal, came as a powerful shock to a world that felt it was conquering disease and in time might conquer ageing and death. This message was stressed by health awareness advertising campaigns that used images such as the tombstone to get their point across.

> *Death is inevitable.*

The renunciation of material things is the only way to follow Christ into His Father's house and eternal life, or the Buddha into Nirvana.

> *Suddenly I came out into a bright, bright light, the area was like a dome, of the kind you put over a clock, light was coming through windows in the top. There was a gold coffin and it was at this point that I felt really frightened and anxious, didn't want to be there, the light felt uncomfortable. The gold coffin in the middle of the room was encrusted with jewels. I climbed into*

it, pulled the lid down over me, all these jewels and gold coins fell down on top of me.

There is in the remedy a dynamic between materialism and death, and the foregoing of material things, of a return to nature and to a spiritual world. This also is reflected in house imagery where the solid house becomes the natural tepee or the South Sea island where housing is unnecessary.

I felt like I had to keep my feet on the ground, the only way to describe it would be as a delusion really—a tribal one; Cheyenne with tepees.

Everything felt natural, tribal—like the South Sea islands, natural barefoot, nothing much underneath, with flowers, natural, with white, green and water.

The house could also be light and filled with music.

The thing that was noticeable about the house was the wood. There was wood everywhere, and floaty white lace. In one room, I think it was the nursery, there was a white lace carpet on the floor. There were West African drummers in some part of that house.

The house that I was organizing the renting of had lots of music in it. A modern room, big room, and very beautiful.

Another particular image was of a house that was large and had not been fully explored: there were secret rooms or floors that had not yet been opened up. Here the house is a metaphor for the life. This too would fit with the appearance of AIDS, a disease of the young that cut down its victims, often very creative people, in their prime when there seemed so much promise unfulfilled.

I felt very playful. If I could give you an image: you have all spoken about houses and rooms; it was as if I had moved. I had fully moved into my house and I can go right up to the window of my house. This isn't a dream or anything, this is an image. Whereas some people are saying they felt persecuted so they would go back into themselves, I actually felt quite safe to go right up to my very extremities and what the hell, it doesn't matter what people say and I can go right up to the window and right into the bay and move right round. So it is the opposite of what everyone is saying.

I felt that there were people who just went terribly serious and I had to move right back from anybody who was serious because the message was that life is too short and the house is too big. Let's explore every room.

The house is also a metaphor for the self—particularly the material self, the body. The house can be old, rambling and decrepit, though often it is being renovated. AIDS patients have an optimism and a thirst for information about the illness and a willingness to try anything that might help.

Big palatial house, used to be very grand, now very ramshackle and being restored by new owners. Striking pictures in the house, modern prints, very, very large—very ornate with large frames, colours stunning and very rich. Woke feeling as if I had eaten a very nice meal.

In some of the dreams, the houses were very different inside from how they appeared on the outside. Sometimes it was a matter of size: the interior was bigger than the exterior; sometimes it was a matter of condition or richness: the interior was far more luxurious than the external presentation. This dissonance is a key theme in the remedy: the internal self is not properly reflected in its outer presentation. The outer perception does not reflect the true internal value.

The house had a top layer which I left derelict so that nobody would suspect that on the basement level I had a beautiful house, so half of it was derelict and half of it was really beautiful downstairs. I don't usually remember dreams and it was distinctive.

I went to a house with the possibility of buying it. It was on the corner in an industrial estate with lots of scrap metal around, but it was only an ordinary house behind a very high wooden fence around it and there were no views because it was contained inside the fence. The house was like a Tardis because it was much larger inside. There was space in the hall and the staircase and the landings were wide and the view from the lounge was of pretty gardens and the view from the upstairs rooms was a view of the rolling fields. It was in need of renovation, it was empty but it was tatty and it needed to be redecorated. My family was with me and there was a very contented feeling as if I was home. It was the difference between the little outside and the big inside that was strange.

A house by a station. Lots of people about. The station was built on top of a roof. It was in a very rundown state. There was a hill leading up to it and a rough fence all around it. Made of wooden paling held together with wire, I think they call it sheep fencing. I met a very scruffy chap and I said to him, "Where are you living now?" I was some sort of authority figure, a teacher perhaps. He said, "I live underneath". We went down to his place. It looked derelict outside, rundown, and I thought, "Nobody could live inside". But inside it was like a palace. There was a huge hall and lots of lovely antique furniture. It was beautiful. I asked him, "How much rent do you pay for this?" It seems he was allowed to live there by the owner.

This dissonance can be around a sense of identity and particularly around issues of gender and sexuality.

Mind going completely blank. Lost all sense of identity—didn't know who I was, found this experience very frightening, I burst into tears.

Felt very sexually aroused by image of young male child.

Noticed that, when I was playing football, I was kicking with my left foot which I never would have done usually.

He also told me that at parties he often used to be approached by men. He had always hated this. Since the proving this has stopped. Now he finds that women are attracted to him, which he is much happier about.

Just as the house is a metaphor for the physical body, so the physical symptoms are often found in places that have a relationship to parts of a house. There is in the remedy a sensitivity where the body and environment interact, particularly the skin and the orifices, which like the windows and doors of a house are points of interaction between the interior and exterior worlds. The skin (walls and roof) is often sensitive, painful and dry. Almost all the orifices of the body (doors and windows) are affected with pain, dryness and sensitivity. The throat, which seems to be one of the most important physical representation of an opening into the body, is also affected. There would also seem to be difficulty in maintaining physical barriers and a common manifestation of this is in haemorrhage.

To sum up: the walls that protect also divide and separate. This results in feelings of isolation and detachment that cumulate in feeling trapped.

These dynamically contrast and alternate with feelings of connection: to family, society and to the divine.

The most dynamic expression of the issues describes the feeling of losing your shell, your personal, portable house; this causes painful vulnerability and exposure but is also exquisite in allowing the possibility of connection.

Differential diagnosis—preliminary suggestions

Acidums: Tiredness and exhaustion. Strong desire for unity.

Arsenicum: Restlessness. Desire for order. Fear of disease.

Carcinosin: Desire for order. Responsible people. Long history of domination by others. Recurring fevers.

Falco p: Breaching the barriers of trust. Feeling used, abused and dirty.

Galla quercina ruber (Oak galls):
              Feels excluded, like a parasite, ugly, contaminates others.

Germanium: Openess for input, but output closed off.

Heroin:	Cut off. Shut out. Contaminated. Feeling humiliated, like scum.
Lacs:	Feelings of rejection and of not belonging.
Lac caninum:	History of abuse. Self-loathing. Feels that she doesn't belong.
Lac humanum:	Do I adhere to my values or those of society? Exclusion.
Mercurius:	Rotten inside, rotten outside. Ulceration. Syphilitic miasm to the fore.

Natrum carb and Natrum mur:
>Theme of semi-permeable membrane—keeping others out. Vesicles.

Ozone:	Rotting, decay. Barriers. Isolation.

Parasite remedies

Platina:	Distancing self from others by feeling taller and better than them, isolation feelings, degradation and dirtiness.
Polystyrenum:	Insulation from others and from own feelings.
Rhus tox:	Feelings of dirtiness inside and lack of trust outside. Afraid of hidden threat of violence; outsiders should keep out. Physical symptoms of cold and flu. Blisters and vesicles.

Rubber (condom): Barrier. Insulation. Disgust.

Scholten, remedies listed in Stage 8:
>Persevering, keeping going, even when under great pressure.

Staphysagria:	History of injury/abuse.
Syphilinum:	Contamination, washing, estranged. Destructive pathology, history of drug abuse. Ulceration.
Thuja:	Feelings of ugliness, unworthiness and secretiveness. The body feels fragile, brittle. Death occurs when the boundary fails and the soul floats free.

CHAPTER 21

FALCO PEREGRINUS—CONSTRAINT VERSUS FREEDOM, MASTER AND SLAVE

A Syphilo-Psoric (AIDS miasm) sarcode

The homeopathic proving of this remedy took place at the School of Homeopathy in 1997. The choice of peregrine falcon was inspired by a case which seemed to indicate the unique features of the bird.

We pick up the patient's story several prescriptions after the initial case-receiving, at a time when she felt increasingly trapped. She was working for a charity and was closeted in the office, raising funds and finding others to go out into the field. During this time, her abusive father also reappeared. Both he and her mother had sexually abused her from the age of 3 until she finally broke away from them at the age of 16. The unanswered question in her mind had always been, "What can I do, what can I say, that will stop them doing this?" She felt menaced and fearful, wanting to escape, yet bound by obligation.

Her case revealed an intensification of a state which had not been alleviated by a third prescription of AIDS 200c, though it was seemingly still well indicated.* The question arose: what substance, plant or creature in nature mirrored her state? Situations of sustained sexual abuse do not arise in the natural world; they are purely a human perversion. So the answer had to lie in something which had a close relationship with humans but which had not yet been proved.

Her situation demanded a remedy even more extreme than Lac caninum or the AIDS nosode, both of which had helped in the past. An answer came to mind in the image of the trained peregrine falcon. The patient loved running and climbing the rugged rock face (peregrines nest on ledges of sheer rock faces). Her story reflected the training of the falcon,

---

* This case is also mentioned in Chapter 20 on AIDS, in the section, 'Curative response to the remedy proving', and may be viewed in full by logging onto www.homeopathyschool.com and linking through to the proving website.

which involves being starved, tied by the ankles and kept prisoner in a dark place. The relationship between falconer and falcon suggests a perverted bond of persecutor and victim. The bird has no prospect of escape until, once trained, it is allowed its flight, returning by conditioned reflex when summoned by the sound of the whistle and the sight of the lure.

When these reflections were shared with the patient, she mentioned that she knew a vet who ministered to an aviary of hunting birds! A wing feather clip and blood spot were procured and sent to the pharmacy to be run up to the 30th centesimal potency. After taking the remedy, the patient lost her fear and sense of disempowerment, quit her stifling job, and is currently living in her beloved Scotland where she can roam free, making her peregrinations.

Themes of the proving

Falco peregrinus is a sterling remedy in cases that feel constrained and dominated, especially by a parent or partner or their own children. They may feel like a trapped wild animal, forced to do things against their instinct for survival. When they break out, it may be with violence, even towards their own children. Their refusal to be subdued gives rise to internal conflict. They may 'numb out', experiencing waves of separation and becoming detached. Then their anger can be cold and destructive. They usually feel deeply connected with nature.

The themes that emerged in the Falco peregrinus proving can be arranged on an axis of opposing forces. At one pole is brightness, clear-sightedness, and laughter (Falco peregrinus has a major 12 noon modality, when the sun is at its highest point). At the opposing pole is the coldness of unfeeling anger, especially towards their own children, and indeed anything perceived as restraint. The feeling for these provers was of being humiliated, scorned, undervalued, and menaced. There is an unfeeling aspect to the remedy, compounded by a sense of being above it all and detached. From this perspective, human life may seem cheap, impoverished and dirty. One prover reported that she had become 'the Ice Queen', while some others said that sex and sensuality were 'off the map'. From this detached perspective, it is natural to seek a purely analytical solution to any emotionally charged situation.

The trained falcon's primal situation of fear and deprivation translates into terms of unfeeling numbness, as with many fear remedies. This response is the natural one, once fight-and-flight have been tested and found wanting. Perhaps arising out of this primal experience, a number of provers felt a marked empathetic response to endangered environments and disempowered people. This response in the captive bird may be as natural as is flight for the free bird.

In the initial stages of the proving, most of the provers felt elevated, clear-sighted, focussed, and close to nature. Many had preoccupations with spiralling and gyring.

The proving dose was taken over the weekend. On Sunday morning, seven of the group, two of them men, came to class with painted fingernails, emblematic of the falcon's death-delivering talons. While driving to a birthday party, all had got confused. Several had a terrible time getting off roundabouts (traffic circles!)—emblematic of the falcon's ascending spiral flight prior to its stoop upon the prey.

The peregrine falcon

The peregrine falcon is one of 38 species of the genus *Falco,* the true falcons, which includes the kestrel and the merlin. However, such is the representative importance of the bird that it gave its name to the *Falconiformes,* the whole order of diurnal (active in the daytime— "GENERALS: noon, afternoon, 14h, 17h") bird of prey that includes eagles, hawks, vultures and buzzards.

Several features distinguish the falcons from other birds of prey. They do not build nests but lay their eggs in 'scrapes', depressions made on cliff ledges, in holes in trees or even on the ground. They have proportionally longer and narrower wings than the eagles and hawks, which makes them stronger and faster in the air but less manoeuvrable close to the ground. They have a 'tomial tooth', a projection on the upper beak with a corresponding notch on the lower one. This serration allows them to kill their prey immediately with a bite to the back of the neck so that they do not generally have to contend with a struggling victim as the hawks do (dreams, "meat", "raw meat"; "biting, bites those around him"; "biting, scratching and clawing").

The peregrine falcon is one of the most cosmopolitan of birds. It was once found almost everywhere except the arid tropical deserts. However, due to pesticide poisoning, it has almost completely disappeared from the Americas east of the Rockies and the Andes.

The falcon's flight takes the form of a series of rapid strokes of the wings followed by a short glide. It usually climbs above its prey and dives onto it. This dive, called the 'stoop', has a speed variously estimated from 100-200 miles per hour, making the peregrine falcon the fastest creature on earth (dreams: "falling", "flying in an aeroplane", "driving a car fast", "kites", "windsurfing"; also dreams of a "wall of water", which is what the falcon would see if it stooped over water; delusions, "elevated in the air and flying", "rushing towards the stars", "motion", "horizon unfolding").

The favourite prey is pigeon but the peregrine will eat almost anything it can catch (dreams: "meat", "pork"; "eating human flesh"). If the prey is not killed by the shock of being hit with razor sharp claws moving at more than a hundred miles an hour, it is quickly dispatched by a bite to the neck. The male brings the food close to the nest and passes it to the female in mid-air. This can be an impressive display as they both fly vertically up, chest to chest, and pass the food from talon to talon.

The fledged birds stay near the nest for another five or six weeks while they learn to fly and hunt. They often chase their siblings in playful games ("blissful"; "carefree"; "cheerful"; "playful") and the adults will drop dead and then live prey near them, teaching the young birds to take their food in mid-air and eventually to hunt. Captive-bred birds that are released into the wild are able to hunt by instinct; but birds that have been taught by their parents or have been trained by a falconer are more successful. These observations help us appreciate the importance of the alliance of trained bird and falconer, and its 'translation' into the bond of victim and persecutor—a bond which is at the heart of cases for which this remedy is the simillimum.

In common with all birds, much time is devoted to grooming and removing ticks, fleas and other pests (dreams: "combing the hair", "infested by woodlice"; "delusions, ugly, body is"; "dreams, dirt").

The name falcon comes from the Latin *falx,* sickle, and alludes to the sharp beak that, like the grim reaper, brings sudden death. Peregrine comes from the Latin *peregrinus,* strange or foreign. This was the term used for non-Roman citizens living in Rome; it later became the description applied to pilgrims ("travelling, desire for"; "speed, desire for"; "confusion of mind, loses his way in well-known streets"). Those falcons living in areas where there is plenty of food during the winter tend to remain near their breeding territories. Others wander considerable distances and those that spend summer and breed in the Arctic are fully migratory, travelling to Africa and South America during the winter months. Some species of falcon cross vast oceans in a single flight: a peregrine has been spotted on a ship more than eight hundred miles from the nearest land ("delusion, space, expansion of ").

Mythology of the peregrine falcon

The peregrine falcon has been regarded as a mystic bird, and as a messenger from another world and a stranger in ours. The North American Indians believe it to be a messenger that brings guidance from the spirit world.

It was in Egyptian mythology that the falcon found its most powerful expression. Horus, which means 'the distant one' or 'that which is above', was the most important of the many falcon gods in Egyptian mythology ("delusion, ice queen, that she is"; "human life seems cheap and dirty").

Osiris and his sister-wife Isis ruled Egypt and had brought agriculture, peace and prosperity. Their brother Seth was jealous and overthrew Osiris, cutting him into small pieces that he dispersed and buried all over Egypt. Isis gathered the pieces of her husband and joined them together. In the form of a kite, she covered his body and with her wings beat air into his mouth, animating him for long enough for him to impregnate her before he departed to rule over the dead.

Horus, the child of this union, was hidden from his uncle in the papyrus marshes of the Nile Delta and brought up in secret by his mother. Horus is often iconographically depicted as a vulnerable child, either suckling at Isis's breast or sitting on her lap sucking her fingers. He is sometimes referred to as 'Horus, the child with his finger in his mouth'. This is a rare iconography; the only other major figures portrayed as being so vulnerable and dependent on their mothers are Christ and Eros ("naïve, open, honest and childlike"; delusions: "glass, she is made of", "transparent, he is", "small, body is smaller"; fears: "approach of others", "attacked", "being bitten", "injury, of being injured"; "sensitive to certain persons"). The secrecy and danger of Horus's upbringing meant that his mother was continually concerned for his welfare. Egyptian people called on Isis to cure a sick child by means of a spell that compared him or her with Horus.

On coming of age, Horus, guided by his mother's guile and forensic skills, set about persuading the court of the gods that the kingdom of Egypt had been usurped by his uncle and was rightfully his (delusions: "persecuted, he is", "repudiated by his relatives", "friendless", "betrayed"). As a sky god, Horus' right eye was said to represent the sun and his left the moon (VISION: "clarity of", "bright, as if someone had turned up the lights", "glittering objects", "acute"; EYE: "brilliant"). In one of the numerous contests and incidents between Horus and Seth, the left eye of Horus was shattered (VISION: "foggy", "blurred", "flashes"). The remedy Falco peregrinus has many rubrics around eyes and vision; and all birds of prey have extraordinary visual powers.

Through the magic of Thoth, Horus' eye was restored to perfection and became the *Udjat,* a human eye surrounded by the falcon's facial markings. This became a symbol of soundness, perfection, protection and purification. It was one of the most potent amulets of protection and is still an immensely powerful icon. The process of the eye's being shattered into small pieces and restored to wholeness was symbolised by the phases of the moon.

After a trial that consumed the gods for over eighty years, Horus won his case against Seth and was awarded the kingship of Egypt. As such, he and the Pharaoh, as god and ruler of Egypt, were one and the same. The hieroglyph of the falcon therefore meant kingship, and always precedes the name of a Pharaoh.

Falconry

The art of hunting with birds of prey has almost certainly been practised for over four thousand years. The earliest record of the practice is a Hittite carving of the 13th century BC in which a child is holding the leash of a jessed falcon ("trapped, feels"; dreams: "trapped", "humiliation", "paralysed"; delusions: "small, body is smaller", "is under superhuman control", "watched, is being", "walls are falling inwards"). There is evidence that the Assyrians were keen falconers. The Egyptians, in spite of their close contact with the Assyrians, never took up falconry, perhaps because of their devotion to Horus. The Greeks and Romans too were never particularly taken with the sport, though it was popular among the Germanic peoples, the Gauls and the Celts. The sport was, as still is, important in the Middle East. During the early Middle Ages, the Moorish invasion of Spain met with the Franks, who were already interested in falconry. The art found a new importance that lasted throughout the Middle Ages and the Renaissance and reached its apogee in the reign of Louis XIII. The French Revolution marked the end of falconry as the sport of kings in Europe.

In the Orient, falconry was part of Japan's Samurai tradition and was widespread in India and Central Asia. Today it is only some of the Arabian princes who have the resources and the will to carry it on as a royal art, but in many countries there remain small numbers of committed falconers and hawkers.

The hunt

On the whole, falconry takes advantage of the birds' natural instincts. A dog is used to 'point' the position of the quarry. The dog stays absolutely still while the falcon is let slip and given time to climb in a circling motion. When the falcon is in position, the dog puts up the quarry and the bird stoops on it at great speed, killing or stunning it. The falcon brings its prey to the ground and, mantling or spreading its wings tent-like over its prey, it begins to pluck its feathers out. The falconer must approach quickly while the bird is engrossed and offer a lure of fresh meat ("delusion, danger, impression of, but without fear", "fear of being attacked, by partner"). The falcon will instinctively take the lure, offering the falconer a chance to snatch the quarry and catch the bird by its jesses. The falcon is given a small part of the kill, the 'faire courtoisie'.

Training

The training of the falcon is necessary in part to make the bird used to people and the accoutrements of the hunt, but most importantly to give the falconer a way of calling the bird back to him. This is done by creating a Pavlovian response to the sight of the lure and the sound of a particular whistle.

The bird, if young or captive-bred, is kept in 'hack', a state of semi-freedom, until its wings are fully grown. It is always fed by the falconer and wears large hacking bells to prevent it from taking its own prey. When ready for training, the falcon is 'furnished' with jesses, lengths of supple but hard-wearing leather, that are attached to each of its legs. The jesses can be attached by a swivel to a creance, a long strong leash, to hold the bird or prevent it from flying away. Jesses are worn all the time, even when the bird is in flight.

The bird is left tethered in semi-darkness without food ("delusions, black, objects and people, sees", "despair, black hole, looking into a", "despair, sensation of being a fully functioning empty shell", "despair, thinks everything is lost", "dreams, cruelty to animals", "detached, waves of detachment", "delusion, enlarged, persons are", "fear, being attacked", "delusion, persecuted", "delusion, separated from the world", "delusion, out of the body and floating in the air", "delusion, is present and simultaneously detached"). After a substantial time, when the bird is exhausted and starving ("delusions, abused, being"), it is offered a morsel of meat on the gloved fist. When it is driven by hunger to eat, it will step onto the glove to take the meat (dreams: "food", "food, horrible/insufficient/revolting", "meat with legs and feet", "raw meat", "meat thrust into mouth"). Gradually the bird gets used to coming to the fist to feed and to being carried around. Hawks are always fed the lure on the fist and are called by being shown the gloved hand. The lure is a horseshoe-shaped piece of padded leather with birds' wings on either side and a ring, to which meat is tied, in the centre. The lure is swung in a circle on a piece of cord (dreams: "roundabouts", "spirals"). Whenever the bird is offered food, a distinctive whistle is sounded.

One prover of Falco peregrinus reported:

> *Something is stirring at the very core of me, holding on to my feelings and emotions, engulfing them. I feel sick, frightened, trapped. My legs feel weak. Something alien is going on—it's not me—but is it? I feel as if I am going mad, divided. I want "it" to come out. I feel as if I could be sick and throw it up and out, but it would have to come from right deep down. It is putting out tentacles. I feel disgusted by its presence. It's trying to control me. It's got hold of me and won't let me go. It's trying to take me over.*

When the bird has become used to people and dogs and to being fed, it is introduced to the hood, which fits over the its head and is tied on with laces ("delusion, sees black objects and people", "visions, black objects", "sees black boots"). The hood is kept on the bird when transporting it and during the hunt to prevent it from becoming distracted or over-excited.

Imagine from the falcon's point of view the experience of travelling hooded in an alien and frightening environment, surrounded by people, horses, and dogs, or today perhaps in the back of a four-wheel-drive through streets. The falcon reacts to frightening situations in two ways: either he wants to escape, or he goes numb ("escape, attempts to", "delusions, has an iron shield around him", "delusions, he is friendless", "danger, lack of reaction to", "delusion, limbs are separated when he is riding in a car").

> *I get a sort of spaciness, especially in the car. The detachment becomes so intense that it starts off with a numbness in my legs. The world seems to disintegrate in front of me. It happens every time I get into a car... The outside felt as if it could disintegrate at any time, like tripping. Waves of detachment came over me.*

The training of the bird continues with the falcon on a gradually lengthening leash or 'creance' and, when the falconer is confident that the bird will return on being called, flying freely.

A bird of prey is never domesticated ("fearless", "joy in nature", "ecstasy, walking in open air", "delusions, she is a reined-in wild stallion that desires to be free", "delusions, flying, rushing towards the stars"). The learned response to the lure and the sound of the whistle will usually call the bird back, but if it were to fly out of sight or hearing, it would be free. Miniature radio trackers are now fitted to trained birds so they can be traced.

Falconers keep close track of the weight of their birds. If a bird is too heavy it will not be hungry and will not be particularly interested in hunting. It will also be less likely to return when called. If it is too light, it will be hungry but may be too weak to hunt properly. The experienced falconer knows his bird's ideal weight and feeds it so that it is at that weight when he wants to fly it. In our experience, cases presenting with eating disorders come within the range of this remedy: not only are falcons trained by withholding and providing food, but the falconer continuously monitors their weight. Various provers reported feelings of self-disgust ("delusions, ugly, body is", "ailments from shame", "ailments from domination", "fear, being poisoned"; dreams: "eating", "insufficient food", "dirt", "cooking meat").

Although the falcon is not the largest or the rarest of the birds of prey, it has always been regarded by falconers as 'the Noble Bird' or 'the Gentle Bird' and has always been the favourite of the true cognoscenti. It is the fastest and most acrobatic of the falcons, and the one most willing to take on something bigger than itself. It is also the bird with the most character, the one that seems the most human. It is often tame and quite easy to train but it can also be the most obstreperous and difficult.

The source of the remedy: Nesbit

The substance of the remedy was taken from Nesbit, a 2-year-old captive-bred peregrine tiercel trained in the traditional way. However, he has never been allowed to fly free, and has always been kept tethered by his jesses. His owner prizes him above all his other birds, and fears that he might fly away. Nesbit is a stud bird, from whom semen is harvested ("ailments from sexual abuse", "sexual humiliation", "delusion, abused", "dreams, coition, forced").

Nesbit was acquired when a very young eyass and was brought up in his owner's home. Even for a peregrine, he is a bird of considerable character and charm.

The remedy was prepared from a small piece of feather and a sample of blood taken from Nesbit by his regular vet.

Culls and pesticides

Although the peregrine falcon arouses extraordinary devotion in many falconers and most bird watchers, in others, particularly pigeon fanciers, it arouses an equally powerful hatred. Ironically, it was this loathing that led to the discovery that the species, and perhaps life on the planet itself, was in imminent danger of annihilation.

During the Second World War, carrier pigeons were still an important means of communication, particularly for bringing messages back to England from occupied France. These birds, which flew steadily and fairly slowly, were favourite meals for peregrine falcons along the south coast of England. Worried that they were losing valuable messages, the RAF ordered a massive cull. Over 600 birds and countless eyasses were killed during the war years. Given that there were about 1100 pairs of birds in the entire country before the war and that the cull was concentrated on the south coast, the action must have killed most of the birds in southern England. After the war, however, numbers recovered surprisingly quickly.

In 1961 English pigeon fanciers claimed that the peregrine falcon population was getting out of hand and that the bird should lose its protected status. The government commissioned the British Trust for Ornithology to conduct a study on falcon numbers. Derek Ratcliffe, who has since written the definitive book on peregrine falcons, carried out the study. To everyone's surprise, he discovered that although numbers had recovered well from the wartime cull, they had begun to fall dramatically in the mid 1950s. He found that the population in 1961 was 68% of the pre-war level and that it fell further to 56% in 1962 and 44% in 1963. When Ratcliffe's findings became known, it was discovered that this decline was a worldwide phenomenon. Falcons, which had once been numerous, were now extinct in the vast forests of Eastern Europe and had completely disappeared from the eastern side of North America.

Tissue studies carried out on dead birds and the addled or broken eggs that were now so common seemed to indicate that pesticides had had a significant role in this decline. Organochlorine chemicals had been developed during the war to kill disease-carrying insects that could have a devastating effect on the health of troops fighting in the tropics. DDT was the most important of these chemicals and throughout the 1950s it was widely used all over the world. Since 1947, pigeon fanciers had dusted their birds with it to kill feather lice. Closer investigation revealed that falcons had suffered a double blow from pesticides. The newer, more powerful organochlorines such as aldrin and dieldrin accumulated in the fat of the birds that the falcons ate, often reaching toxic levels that killed the predators outright. At the same time DDE, a product of DDT breakdown, accumulated in the falcons and interfered with an enzyme that is important in the production of eggshells. The shells became so thin that they often broke under the weight of the brooding mother (delusions: "poisoned", "pollution, environmental", "being poisoned", "cruelty to animals"; "fear, being injured").

The thinning eggshells relate to the AIDS nosode theme of the thinning boundary, and the remedy Falco peregrinus is found within the AIDS miasm. Boundaries keep what is in, in; and what is out, out. AIDS is characterised by a complete breakdown of the immune system which stands as the boundary between our bodies and foreign substances.*

These discoveries led to restrictions in the use of these pesticides and when Ratcliffe conducted follow up surveys he found numbers almost back up to 1961 levels by 1971; in 1981 they were up to 90% of pre-war levels. The British peregrine falcon does not tend to travel much and in the UK, recovery was happily quite rapid. In North America and Eastern Europe, the birds tended to migrate, wintering in tropical areas where DDT was still used. They were completely wiped out. In much of Europe, they are still extinct. In North America a program of releasing captive-bred birds has led to a population of a few hundred pairs but there is a long way to go. Even in the virgin expanses of the Canadian Arctic, falcons are being killed by the DDT still being sprayed in Central and South America, which they and their prey ingest during winter migrations.

---

* See Chapter 19 on the AIDS nosode.

Just as the falcon is at the top of his food chain, so man is at the top of his; the fate that almost befell the falcon might yet happen to him. The story of the falcon and pesticides plays a major part in the realisation that mankind has in his power the ability to destroy the world in which he lives. This realisation, backed up by Rachel Carson's book Silent Spring, led to an awareness of ecology and the birth of the green movement. It also resulted in a terror for what might happen and a feeling that we are responsible for whatever happens to us ("injustice, cannot support", "horrible things, sad stories affect her profoundly", "fear, drought", "joy in nature", "ecstasy, sublime, in nature").

The environmental movement brings to mind the role of the funerary falcon god Horus, who, among other functions, was the psychopompus who led the living into death and the dead into their new life upon the wheel of cyclical return.

Abstract from the proving

MIND THEMES:
  Spirals, waves and colours.
  Carefree/Careless. Freedom and speed.
  Floating and flying.
  Giggling and innocence.
  Groups.
  Empathy with people and nature.
  Clarity. Confidence.
  Apprehension.
  Swearing and squandering. Anger.
  Coldness. Unfeeling.
  Small and vulnerable.
  Hemmed in.
  Controlled.
  Scorned. Humiliation.
  Guilt.
  Apathy. Isolation and despair.

GENERALS:
< Stormy weather. Cold.
> Warmth. Mountains.
Wavelike sensations.

FOOD AND DRINKS:
Desire: Alcoholic drinks. Pickles. Meat.
Aversion: Coffee. Cucumbers. Tomatoes.
> Beer.

VERTIGO/HEAD:
Vertigo as if intoxicated, morning on waking.
Coldness, head, as if cold air came from head.
Pain > hard pressure; alternating sides.

EYE/VISION:
Stitching left eye, with left-sided headache.
Bright vision. Images retained too long.

FACE:
Expression absent, cold distant.
Stiffness and pain lower jaw.

MOUTH/TEETH:
Tongue feels soft and numb.
Painful ulcers.

THROAT/EXTERNAL THROAT:
Catarrh with tenacious mucus.
Rash on external throat.

STOMACH/ABDOMEN/RECTUM/STOOL:
Sensation as if something alive in stomach.
Hard stomach. Distention > stool.
Twitching and jerking right side.
Diarrhoea alternating with constipation.

FEMALE GENITALIA:
Menses copious and short.

Sore pain vagina during coition, while urinating.

CHEST:
Eruptions mammae, nipples, painful to touch.

Pain mammae, nipples, < left.

BACK:
Pain, tension and stiffness cervical region, < morning on waking; as if back would break.

EXTREMITIES:
Awkwardness.

Heaviness lower limbs < morning on waking.

Nails grow rapidly, are hard and thick.

Cold, clammy perspiration < hands.

Separated sensation in limbs, < driving.

SKIN:
Dry. Cracked. Shrivelled.

Pimples bleeding, inflamed, painful.

Differentials

AIDS: Feeling persecuted, dirty and humiliated. Close to nature.

Anacardium: Cruelty.

Carcinosin: History of domination.

Lac caninum: Feeling dirty and humiliated.

Platina: Cold, haughty, the Ice Queen.

Sepia: Being forced against her will.

Staphysagria: Humiliation.

Thuja: Dirty, worthless.

Other birds of prey.

Miasms

Falco peregrinus is an example of the AIDS miasm, combining the Syphilitic notes of feeling dirty and above it all (as birds of prey do) with the AIDS feelings of having boundaries violated, of being used and abused. The issue of ownership is central: the falconer's prize possession is the falcon, a captive of the conditioned reflex to return to the owner's glove. Nesbit, the bird from whom the remedy was prepared, is never allowed to fly free ("delusion, trapped"). He is a stud falcon from whom semen is harvested ("ailments from sexual abuse", "sexual humiliation", "delusion, abused", "dreams, coition, forced"). These themes are relevant not only in sexual relationships but also in those between partners and parents and children, where the issue is of the boundary being too closed or too open (Psoric notes), or violated (the AIDS note).

PART IV

CONCLUSION

CHAPTER 21

DEVELOPMENTAL MODEL OF MIASMS

This last chapter provides a summary of the developmental model of miasms based upon their evolution in pace and depth of invasion. To recapitulate Hahnemann's three miasms:

- First miasm, Psora—eruption of the skin, which, if suppressed, becomes the developmental platform for all further disease. Psora has the fastest development from contagion to initial symptom production, but slowest overall evolution of chronic disease;

- Second miasm, Sycosis—relatively quick development from contagion to initial symptoms, and medium-paced overall evolution of chronic disease. Here the infectious agent, the gonococcus, inflames the mucous membranes of the urinary-generative tract before penetrating more deeply into the organism, typically developing iritis, rheumatism, warts and heart valve disease;

- Third miasm, Syphilis—slowest development (a protracted dormant phase) followed by fast overall evolution of chronic disease. Here the infectious agent, the spirochete, destroys the interior of the cell, eventually attacking the most interior structures: the bones and central nervous system.

Hahnemann's triad is fundamental and sufficient for an understanding of the further miasms posited by us and other homeopaths. It has to be understood that Hahnemann's definition has been extended to include the taints of non-infectious, non-venereal diseases which are nonetheless transmitted by inheritance (genetic mutation), weakening the inherent susceptibility of the constitution. The further miasms are:

- Tubercular miasm—a mixture of Syphilis and Psora;
- Cancer miasm—a mixture of Sycosis and Syphilis;
- AIDS miasm—a mixture of Psora and Syphilis.

From a historical perspective, tuberculosis (famously a 19th century disease), cancer (which escalated rapidly in the 20th century) and AIDS (currently escalating, especially in Africa) have followed on each other's tails over the last 200 years.

Rajan Sankaran's miasm map is similar to the one presented in this book. It differs primarily at the front end, 'unpacking' the Psoric miasm into Acute, Typhoid, Ringworm and Malarial miasms, but then it conforms, with Sycotic being followed by Cancer, Tubercular, Leprous (which overlaps AIDS miasm). Sankaran places the Syphilitic miasm last in the series, while our model has Syphilis as one of Hahnemann's first three miasms and subsequent miasms as mixtures of the first three. Sankaran's concept of miasms (while elegant as well as practical) is different from the concept underlying the model in this book. For Sankaran, the miasms represent the pace, depth and desperation to which the vital sensation or uncompensated state is experienced in any disease.

**Miasms and signatures in three nosodes
of mixed miasmatic character**

Tuberculinum is associated with restless discontent. This situation might arise for an individual who feels trapped in a restrictive and inimical environment. His best option, given the suffocative feelings that he experiences, is to break free. Once he has done so, he usually feels that there is no going back—it is an irrevocable declaration of adolescent dissent. These assertions, give their destructive nature, are primarily driven by the Syphilitic aspect of the miasm. Tuberculosis is derived from a disease that typically arises in populations and societies that have been dispossessed. Their fixed posture, their stuck place, is that their home, land and culture has been irrevocably lost. Therefore, they are restlessly searching for a new resting-place, but cannot find it. This severance from the protective home is essentially a Psoric expression, characterised by forsaken feeling, poverty and longing. It has been altered by violent upheavals such as war and famine, giving the typically Syphilitic modulation for which Tuberculosis is known.

Carcinosin is associated with suppression of ego drives—the 'unlived life' syndrome which so often underpins the cancer patient's story, the Psoric note—and striving for conformity (in this respect demonstrating its relationship with Lac humanum, human milk). In children, an uncompensated state often prevails, typified by difficult, contrary and defiant behaviour, while in adults, a suppressed state typified by fastidiousness and well-mannered behavior is usually seen. It is common for patients requiring Carcinosin, should they be fastidious, to express it as a drive for matching things.

The nosode is derived from diseased tissue which is characterised by overabundant proliferation of cells of one type, like bricks in a wall. The cells represent a monomania of conformity. Cancers are only limited because their unruly proliferation destroys the host organism. Sycosis is the leading miasm, in the sense that the desire for more and more is expressed by the unruly growth of the tumour, with strong Syphilitic (destructive) tendencies.

We have projected our carcinogenic patterns into the world around us, for is not a vast monocultured field of one species of plant a perfect analogy to a cancer?

On a molecular level, plastics such as polythene, polypropylene and polystyrene are similar to tumours, being compounds whose molecule is formed from a large number of repeated units. The units seamlessly join themselves up to form three-dimensional structures. Because no electrons are available to react with other substances, plastics are relatively inert and take centuries to break down in the environment—recalling the cancer tumour's lack of symbiosis with other cells and its resistance to immune system activity. Used for everything from food packaging to furniture, plastics are cheap, ubiquitous and manufactured in vast quantities. The children's toy, Lego, which enjoys such universal appeal, is made of plastic bricks. Lego-land housing estates designed with standardised computer programs are also an expression of the conformity of the cancer miasm.

Mass communication has granted certain TV programmes worldwide popularity, providing the basis for common thinking and responding. Conformity, wherever it rules, belongs to the cancer miasm, while when the note is that of invading personal boundaries, keeping you glued to the screen against your better judgement, then the Aids miasm is invoked.

AIDS: The AIDS nosode is associated with boundary issues: keeping what is in, in; and what is out, out. The disease is characterised by a complete breakdown of the immune system.

In health, the vital force through the medium of the immune system reacts homeostatically to morbific influences, throwing them off: keeping what is out, out. Examples on the physical level are acute displays such as fevers, discharges, diarrhoea and pus. Examples on an emotional level include shouting, hitting, moaning and tears. However, should the individual become encumbered by disease through a deficiency of acute responses, due to miasmic predisposition, social suppression or drug use, then chronic disease will settle in. In this aspect, the AIDS nosode, because it is failing to externalise, is similar to Carcinosin. Underpinning both nosodes is the ubiquitous Psoric influence.

The relationship between AIDS nosode and Lac humanum is noteworthy. In Rajan Sankaran's provings of Lac humanum, as in the AIDS proving, themes of houses, self-loathing and rejection came prominently into the foreground. Not surprisingly, milk and blood have features in common. Milk is derived from blood. As blood circulates through the body, it 'touches' every cell, bringing to mind the AIDS nosode theme of belonging and its opposite of feeling outcast. The key common theme of AIDS nosode and Lac humanum is relationships, how we nurture and how we touch or don't touch. Part of the Lac humanum idea is 'good mother, bad mother' (partly because the mother's influence helps to socialise us); the AIDS idea is that of blood brothers, 'good brother, bad brother'—trust and its opposite, betrayal. Blood brothers can be a group or tribe, like the gay community. However, gay anal sex involves touching blood in a potentially disease-creating way.

In Lac humanum, the central issue revolves around individuality versus conforming to the group; self-interest versus helping others; going off and doing one's own thing versus staying at home and attending to family obligations. The opposite of Lac humanum's individuality theme is universality. This, as we have already posited, is similar to the AIDS theme: "I flow into you and you flow into me." The opposite of Carcinosin's theme of conformity is "I shall not do what you want of me—get out of my space!" The opposite of AIDS' theme of no barriers is "I am completely separate from you". As Lac humanum is about the price of individuality, Carcinosin is primarily about the price of conformity, and AIDS is about the complete breakdown of defences and barriers. The key concept of AIDS is chronic weakness at the boundary. The positive outcome is freedom to experience love; the negative is feeling excluded, rejected, isolated.

Following the theme of blood brothers, the ideal of the Aquarian age is the brotherhood of humankind. Here the barriers between us are dismantled and we learn to provide for each other. The 'Global Village' ideal of fair play and fair trade becomes established. We come to understand the implications of sharing the planet's resources: the air that we breathe, the oceans, the land. We share the information of all nations via optical and electronic means. What we do and think is transmitted via satellites into our homes, providing us with the choice of staying in touch, and staying in agreement with one another. This democratisation of information could result in a giant step in human evolution.

On the negative side we note that the collapse of the immune defence system is mirrored in world ecology by such phenomena as the ozone hole. The analogy rests upon the fact that a healthy upper atmosphere acts as a barrier to harmful radiation. Ecological homeostasis gone awry, as evidenced by the current crisis of global warming, is another aspect of the AIDS miasm—the biosphere warms up because it cannot let out enough of the heat it absorbs. The barrier has become too impermeable. (The homeopathic proving of Germanium reveals a remedy with a similar theme. Peter Fraser suggests that Germanium is to the AIDS miasm as Sulphur is to the Psoric miasm, and Thuja is to the Sycotic.) On a smaller scale, the rampant diseases of crops in a monoculture are similar to immune system breakdown. They are combated by agricultural chemicals in a manner mirrored by the multiple drug therapies employed in the conventional treatment of AIDS related diseases.

Increasingly, crops are being genetically engineered to confer selective resistance to pests and herbicides. Genetic engineering, like HIV, subverts not only the barrier of the cell but its very centre, the nucleus, and thus may be immediately recognised as related to the AIDS miasm. In a healthy ecology, plants, bacteria, insects and animals interact for the benefit of the whole. This wide-ranging symbiosis represents a 'make love, not war' attitude in nature. The barriers protecting individual species remain intact because they are not threatened by the overcrowding of monocultures. In human terms, any war where land boundaries are breached is an expression of the Aids miasm, as is personal abuse, whether sexual or other abuse, because the boundary of the self has been violated.

It is worthy of note that AIDS was becoming rampant in 1983, when Pluto had entered Scorpio, an event associated with plagues by some astrologers. We could unpack the meaning of this slow-moving astrological configuration as personal and ancestral shit hitting the fan! During this period the world was uncovering child abuse. Also around this time, Chiron, the asteroid associated by astrologers with wounding and healing, was discovered. The primary significance of Chiron could be summed up in the phrase, "suffering is the passport". As a colleague, Ian Marrs, put it, "the flaw is the floor". In other words, the wound forms the basis on which healing can take place. The wound of the AIDS miasm is also the foundation of its healing—the breakdown of the barrier allows compassion and love to come in.

An evolutionary map of miasms, tuberculosis, cancer and AIDS

In the beginning there was the continuum (Eden)
then
separation (the Fall of Man)
(this 'drive' establishes all religions)

alone and abandoned
PSORA
hypofunction/introspection

proliferation—more and more   destruction—less and less
SYCOSIS   **SYPHILIS**
hyper-expansion   hyper-contraction
i.e. excesses of life   i.e. excesses of death

Psora & Syphilis
Separation, abandonment + destruction = homelessness
TUBERCULAR miasm

Sycosis & Syphilis
Proliferation + destruction = more and more of less and less
CANCER miasm

Syphilis & Psora
Violation and destruction of the boundaries of the self
AIDS miasm

Syphilis Pure
Destruction and death—the end of physical life

Finally, about treating patients

As we observe from our daily practice, patients in Western countries are becoming more chronically sick—not just older people but also youngsters. To try to keep up with this trend, homeopaths are proving new remedies that develop symptoms of mixed miasmatic character that are relevant to our evolving situation of degeneration and worsening inheritance.

From the perspective of the health of future generations it would be best that the outward expressions of diseases be left untreated by medical intercessions. This injunction refers to children's inoculation programmes also. *Leave the symptoms alone!* They are the organism's venting mechanisms. If diseases cannot be expelled, they then invade deeper levels causing genetic mutations which in turn pass on miasmic predispositions for disease to future generations. Instead of passively witnessing this, or worse, actively promoting it by suppressing symptoms, we are well advised to focus attention upon the disturbance at the centre—the uncompensated state at the origin of the disease. By making a misamatic analysis of our patients we shift our attention in this direction. Then we can better appraise which symptoms are to be considered and which may be discarded in any individual case.

APPENDICES

APPENDIX 1

MODELS FOR POTENCY SELECTION

There is no consensus within the homeopathic profession on potency selection. This was a precedent set by Hahnemann himself, who continued to experiment with dose, potency and repetition (posology), even after his definitive statements on LM potencies in the 6th edition of the *Organon*.

Let us step backward in time and recapitulate Hahnemann's discovery of potentisation. This was undoubtedly based upon his knowledge of both alchemy and chemistry. After rendering the remedy into soluble form, he submitted it to a series of vigorous shakes (succussions). He discovered on administering these prepared remedies that the progressive dilutions were not only less toxic but also more potent at healing. Hahnemann called this process of serial dilution followed by vigorous shaking 'dynamisation' or 'potentisation'. The main objective was to attenuate noxious side effects while increasing the medicinal activity.

If the remedy was soluble in water and alcohol, he mixed one part of the expressed liquid substance (mother tincture) with 99 parts of water and alcohol and then subjected it to a series of vigorous succussions. This dynamised solution he called the first centesimal potency, designated as 1c. He then mixed one part of this 1c solution with 99 parts water and alcohol and once again succussed the mixture to produce a 2c potency. He then mixed one part of this 2c solution with 99 parts water and alcohol and succussed the mixture to produce a 3c potency. And so on ...

If the substance was not soluble in water or alcohol, it was ground in a pestle and mortar (triturated) with crystallised sugar of milk. A similar process of serial dilution to that with liquids was devised by him, whereby successive dynamisations were created in the solid state until 3c had been reached. At this point Hahnemann was able to dissolve the sugar of milk in water and alcohol and proceed with aqueous dymanisations. This methodology can be easily mechanised, enabling machines in modern pharmacies to supply all remedies in a range of potencies up to and including 1,000,000.

Kent, at the turn of the twentieth century knowing only earlier editions of Hahnemann's *Organon,* up and including the 5th edition, (but not the 6th edition with its description of a new posology, the LM method) correlated harmonic theory with potency, coming up with a series of steps. This was inspired by his research and reading of Emmanuel Swedenborg, the mystic, who commented on the harmonic correspondence between macro- and micro-cosm. These views of Kent and his series of potencies: 6, 30, 200, 1000 (1M), 10,000 (10M), 50,000 (50M), 100,000 (CM), 1,000,000 (MM), were quickly adopted by the homeopathic community world-wide.

It awaited the translation into English of the belated 6th edition of the *Organon* for Hanhnemann's evolving view of remedy administration to be generally known. By this time, Kent's methods had been established and few saw the need to alter what was working well. Thus it is only latterly that homeopathic prescribers have delved into the 6th edition and begun experimenting with the LM range of potentised remedies.

(*Organon* 6th edition, para. 270) To make an LM1 remedy one grain of the powder of the third centesimal potency is diluted in 500 drops of a mixture of alcohol and water. One drop of this is then diluted 1:100 and succussed one hundred times making a dilution which Hahnemann designated LM1 (500 x 100). Poppy-seed sized granules are then moistened with one drop of this solution to create LM1 remedies.

To make an LM2 remedy one poppy-seed granule of LM1 is dissolved in one drop of water and then diluted 1:100 and succussed a further 100 times. Poppy seed granules are then moistened with one drop of this solution to make an LM2. This process is repeated to extend the LM potency range.

In practice we usually only use LM1 to LM10 with exceptional extensions up to the thirtieth.

There are many ways to administer LM's. One of the most user-friendly ways is to use a 15ml dropper bottle. We have two options:

1. We can buy the poppy seed LM potencies from a pharmacy and then make up an LM bottle for the patient by dissolving one granule in alcohol/water in the dropper bottle.
2. We can ask the pharmacy to make up the LM potency in liquid form in the bottle for the patient.

1 to 4 drops taken from the dropper bottle are diluted in a small measure of drinking water (like a tot of whiskey in quantity) in a glass. This is then swished and swilled in the mouth before swallowing. This constitutes one dose of the medicine. Between each dose the dropper bottle is succussed between 2 and 10 times. This dynamises the remedy so that it becomes slightly more potent on a daily basis. LM's are very flexible:

- We can adjust the number of drops taken (in LM's the volume of remedy is significant whereas with centesimal potencies 4 tablets or 1 tablet taken at the same time is still only equal to one dose).
- We can double dilute the dose—that is, take a few drops out of the medicine glass and mix it into a further quantity of drinking water in a second glass.
- We can adjust the repetition of the remedy. We can take 2 doses a day, and in acute work every 5-10 minutes or one dose every two to three days.
- We can adjust the number of succussions.

We need to assess carefully what is happening—if cure is progressing well we may wish to increase the number of drops, repetitions or succussions—if there is any aggravation we may wish to decrease these variables. Any aggravations with LM's should be very short term. During aggravations Hahnemann advises that the medicine be stopped until the intensified symptoms abate. Once this crisis has passed the remedy bottle is succussed again and further doses are taken from it until further progress to cure is once again established.

Hahnemann states that dosing should start with LM1 and then move up to LM2, LM3 and so forth, once each bottle is exhausted. However, present day prescribers may vary these instructions, for instance, some prefer to start with LM2 or 3 and then progress upwards.

There is an obvious attraction to the LM methodology. Repeated and increasingly potent doses are intended to establish cure incrementally and gently. Yet we have seen this method deliver anything but guaranteed gentle cures. Uncomfortable reactions, sharp aggravations and spurious proving effects have occurred. These have been every bit as severe as those initiated by centesimal doses.

We have found that the step to a higher LM once a bottle is finished is often causative of this mischief. It would appear that some individuals' homeostatic response is upset by too rapid a change of potency and that the LM step is too abrupt. In some chronic cases, we have experimented with keeping LM1 going for much longer than Hahnemann recommends, even for several months, and then, once the bottle is empty, moving on by a Korsakovian step. This entails shaking out the bottle so it is quite empty but for the inner surface adhesion of the old potency, and then filling the bottle two-thirds full with fresh alcohol/water and succussing 40 times. This then stands in for LM2, although it carries the memory of the earlier succussions. Subsequent doses are taken in the LM fashion from this refreshed bottle until it in turn is finished. Further dynamisations may be carried out in the same manner. So far, we have had good results using this method.

The purpose of dynamisation is to increase medicinal action on the vital plane, while incrementally reducing the material substance. Our chosen potency and repetition should accomplish this with minimal aggravation before cure.

In addition to working with LM potencies, we have greater experience with the use of the centesimal range of potencies.

Thinking by analogy

The practice of homeopathy requires the practitioner to match the pattern of the disease to the pattern of the remedy. It primarily requires thinking by analogy. It operates by noting the correspondence between things. Using this model, we may suppose a correspondence between potency and the ability of the patient to eliminate or exteriorise the disease. As Hahnemann explains, this is done by producing symptoms. Therefore, it follows that the more vivid and expressive the symptoms, the higher the potency the prescriber may use. This postulate is proven correct in acute work, where it is ever reconfirmed that high potencies stimulate the fastest healing response. Similarly, in childhood epidemics, sporadic acutes, or simply teething troubles, it is noted that higher potencies work best. For this reason, many practitioners' travelling first aid kits are in the 200 centesimal potency or above.

We accept the postulate that increases in potency correspond to increases in the capacity for vital response by the organism. In common with other commentators, we postulate that one key to potency selection lies in determining neither the vitality nor the susceptibility of the patient, but rather in obtaining a sense of the patient's resistance to cure. For it is the natural tendency for an organism to rid itself of the encumbering disease. It is only the resistance it meets along the way that inhibits cure. Therefore, the useful question to ask is:

To what degree might the factors that block the path to exteriorisation of the disease impede progress to cure?

In the light of this simple consideration, a checklist (for opening a case) might look like this:

Go high (200c–MM):

- when the path to exteriorisation of the disease is unblocked (and usually in acute work).

Stay low (6c–30c and LM1):

- when the path to exteriorisation of the disease is blocked.

When a good enough remedy cannot be found, mother tinctures and herbal preparations may be useful, for instance, when helping an organ in distress. In advanced cancer, for example, where tissues are threatened, it is of service to prescribe in this manner. Elimination of drugs, establishment of good habits, and drinking plenty of water, may all help to clarify an unclear homeopathic picture. So, of course, does a rigorous detox regimen.

We find that it is usually better to wait, while staying in touch with the patient at regular and frequent intervals, than it is to prescribe without precision even though partially indicated remedies can and often do remove certain symptoms, temporarily alleviating the patient. This is so because the partially indicated remedy cannot stimulate the vital force to eliminate the disease in its entire extent. The prescriber is easily drawn into colluding with the disease, because the disease wishes to hide itself, as it were, and continue its existence unmolested. The patient's vital force responds to the activity of the disease and the remedy conjointly by producing more symptoms. The prescriber is therefore likely to continue to prescribe partial remedies. A succession of partial remedies does no more than further cover up the true picture of the disease, which continues to do mischief, unchecked, within the interior of the organism, only to spring forth later in the form of a more degenerative condition than the one which first presented.

Another reason to hold back on ungrounded or partially grounded prescriptions is that inadvertent provings may occur. We are hot on this point because our experience with patients and with homeopathic provings daily reconfirms the power of potentised remedies to effect profound changes. Inadvertent provings brought about by the administration of spurious remedies may muddy the water because the prescriber may think that the new symptoms are part of the patient's picture. Proving symptoms add to the patient's suffering. (This is only acceptable when accompanied by marked amelioration of presenting symptoms.) It is often more difficult to find the simillimum after such events. In the face of lack of clarity, it is more efficient and compassionate to delay the administration of potentised remedies until enough information has been gathered about the nature of the patient and the disease to make an informed prescription.

In the light of these impediments to exteriorisation, we can enlarge on the earlier checklist as follows:

Stay low 6c–30c (or use LMs) and repeat until action is established:

- when frank pathology exists (don't blow the fuse!);
- when the patient presents with a complex miasmatic background;

- when vitality is vitiated because of the above reasons and in cases of drugging (including homeopathic over prescribing);
- when there are obstacles to cure such as destructive family dynamics, oppression, suppression and blocked creative outlets;
- when astrological aspects (especially to Saturn) and difficult progressions would slow down cure;
- in situations of geopathic or environmental stress.

The above considerations are not new, nor do they shed light upon how to choose a potency at the high end of the potency scale when the path of disease exteriorisation is not overtly blocked. Their value lies in the fact that, as an easily applied checklist of considerations, they provide a fledgling prescriber with a user-friendly toolkit. Remaining with lower potencies in all but the most clear cut cases is certainly a safe option, and one may always increase potency incrementally once a positive action has been established. However, the model based upon the analogy of remedy potency to vital response has not been fully explored. In order to do this, we must examine ways in which vital responses manifest.

The two teachers responsible for the 'new wave' in homeopathy in Britain in the late 1960's, Thomas Maugham and John Damonte, brought a deeper understanding (codified by the theosophical tradition) to homeopathic philosophy. Of relevance here was their take on the analogous relationship of potency to planes of consciousness. The scheme relates mind, emotions and body to three planes of potency: high, medium and low.

This idea is not supported by work in the field of remedy provings. It has been established that the potency used during a proving has little or nothing to do with each prover's response. Low potencies can and do produce subtle effects upon emotional and mental symptoms, while high potencies can and do immediately bring forth physical sensations and alter physical states. This is elucidated by the explanation that individual prover's innate susceptibility sets the scene within which their responses manifest.

The elemental model of constitutional types

Although unfamiliar to many of us in the field of potency selection, the elemental model is of fundamental significance in other fields of understanding, such as astrology. It has its roots in ancient soils—Chinese, Hindu, Egyptian, Islamic, Greek and hence comes to us. The teaching of the four elements is of particular relevance because the system describes and categorises an individual's make-up and their innate susceptibility. (Hence providing an explanation for a prover's individual area of response to the proving potency).

We may base potency selection upon considerations of the elemental progression of fire, air, water, and earth - that is, upon the increasing materiality of formative forces as they progress from subtle to gross manifestation. This has obvious appeal because it mirrors homeopathic pharmacy, which starts in earth (usually with mineral, plant or animal material) and progresses via succussions and dilutions to the ever more subtle (less material) realms of water, air and fire. Given below is the schema in reverse, where we begin in the realm of energy/spirit and descends into matter.

- Fire, essentially heat, is an energy and without substance.
- Air, being a vapour, is almost immaterial.
- Water is fluid, not yet as formed and solid, as Earth.
- Earth is most dense and represents the ultimate stage in the process of evolving mass.

In this organisation, each element represents a densification or materialisation of energy. The descending series represents the journey from spirit to matter, while, as we have written, during homeopathic pharmacy, remedies start in Earth/matter and progress to Fire/spirit.

The ancient Greek philosopher Heraclitus wrote: "each of the four elements lives by the death of the others: Earth lives by the death of Water; Water lives by the death of Air; Air lives by the death of Fire." In other words, the essence of the superior elemental force must die into the matrix of its inferior in order to imbue it with vitality and existence.

The four psychological functions described by C.G. Jung, namely Intuition, Thinking, Feeling, Sensation, correspond to Fire, Air, Water and

Earth. Jung described how these functions operate in the human psyche (here in the order of Earth, Water, Air and Fire) as follows:

"There are four aspects of psychological orientation, beyond which nothing fundamental remains to be said. In order to orient ourselves we must have

- a function which ascertains that something is there (Earth/Sensation);
- a second function which states whether it suits us or not, whether we wish to accept it or not (Water/Feeling);
- a third function which establishes what it is (Air/Thinking);
- a fourth function which indicates where it came from and where it is going (Fire/Intuition)."

The Bhagavad-Gita (early Vedic scripture) teaches that there is a fifth element, Akasha, translated as space or Ether. Ether is the mediating element between spirit and matter, the arena in which the four other elements play out into the material world. In terms of the makeup of the individual human being, Ether stands between the four elements of the material world (Earth, Water, Fire and Air) and the three subtle elements, ego, intellect, mind (in descending order, with ego or I-ness the most subtle). Ether may be conceived as being related to primal substance or essence, and in this sense is the original, undifferentiated quality of life itself as well as the vital quality of matter - it mediates between primal essence and the myriad forms of matter.

Some characteristics associated with elemental Fire

Elemental fire is associated with intuition—understanding in a flash of inspiration. It is further associated with spiritual aspiration, divine love and sexual desire. It typically expresses as image. Fire also burns, cauterises, cleanses and destroys.

Fire combines two basic qualities: light and heat. The Latin word for fire, *ignis,* whence we derive our term 'ignite', is in turn derived from the Sanskrit word for the God for fire: Agni, the divine messenger and mediator. In Hindu temples the priest burns camphor, the flame conveying mortal prayers to the God. In every Roman Catholic church there burns a perpetual flame which is only extinguished when the church is deconsecrated. Images of God, and of divine messengers such as Christ and the Buddha, illuminating ignorance, representing the warmth of love and the light of truth, are illustrative of the qualities of Fire. The renaissance Italian philosopher Marcilio Ficino wrote: "Just as there are three main powers of fire—heat, light and fleeting subtlety—so there are three similar powers in the soul's essence—the power of life, of understanding and of desiring." In this sense Fire is the principle elemental thrust of what Jung termed individuation—self-realisation.

Elemental Fire is associated primarily with the organs of vision, both the physical eyes and imagination. Passion in any form is an expression of Elemental Fire. This may be a raging mania, it may be religious, it may be sexual, for these all fill us with experiences of absolute commitment and self-forgetting. We are self-forgetting in anger—of the kind that flashes like a flame, such as the anger of Christ when he cast the money lenders out of the temple. We are self-forgetting in religious ecstasy and sexual joy. Small wonder that practices such as Tantric Yoga conjoin them, while Christian and many other religious practices separate them, perhaps intuiting that too much Fire would have an unbalancing outcome, leading to deadly *hubris,* as the Greeks termed personal identification with the Gods.

Some characteristics associated with elemental Air

Elemental air is primarily associated with thinking—it seeks knowledge by processes of discrimination. It manifests by evolving concepts and seeking meaning. The dark side of elemental air is ontological uncertainty, fear of death and delusions of separation.

Air combines two basic qualities: dark and chill. It represents the opposite state of Fire. For this reason it also has similar core issues—for the poles are both representative of the whole. Its image is the frosty midnight, midwinter sky of the new moon. The quality is cutting clarity, cold reason and that species of compassion which exists at the knife edge by which untruth is cut away and only clarity remains. Because Air does away with aspects of raw passion and animal heat, its quality is to enable unencumbered reason to dissect primal experiences with the scalpel blade of the intellect. Air seeks meaning, while fire seeks God. From a religious mystic's perspective, death of passion (greed, hatred and longing) is the goal of life.

On the negative polar extreme of Air, when the Fire of anger is frozen, murder may be perpetrated. When the Fire of inspiration, with its embracing vision, is chilled by cold reason, its vitality may be destroyed, the life killed by the analysis. Love is an expression of Fire, indifference is an expression of Air. At its highest octave, the voice of Air sings the song of eternity and infinity. This music spirits us away from incarnation into death before the return to another life, which, from the perspective of Air, is both instantaneous and eternally delayed, both never and forever. At its lowest octave Air imbalances fill us with dread and fear of death, with desolation, isolation feelings, delusions of the Hell realm and suicidal inclinations. Sustained hatred, homicidal thoughts, racial cleansing, all the atrocities of war, when wrongs are turned into rights, are under the dark dominion of Air in its negative functioning.

Some characteristics associated with elemental Water

Elemental water is primarily associated with feeling—it seeks meaning by processes of dissolution and merging and then finds itself again. It manifests by moods.

Water combines two basic qualities: moisture and fluidity. The symbol which most vividly exemplifies this is the ocean in all her moods, and also lakes, rivers and ponds. Reflecting the ever changing patterns of clouds, light and sky, being subject to wind (and the oceans and bodies of water in general, to the moon's gravity) water is a changeable element. On the other hand when water is unaffected by gravity, as it is in an orbiting spacecraft, then it assumes a perfectly spherical shape. It contains and circumscribes itself. Water seeks itself, joins up with itself. All rivers flow into the larger body of the ocean. Likewise, an elemental Water experience is both containing (as the larger contains the lesser) and dissolving (as the lesser flows into the larger). In respect of the individual ego this brings about dissolution, merging the one with the collective and giving an intimation to the soul of universal containment—a spiritual womb, if you will. Water may also leach out and pull apart our closely held ideas and opinions (Earth) evoking new dimensions—this is likely to liberate feelings which may formerly have been guarded, of which weeping is the natural Watery expression. The fluidity of Water is symbolically representative of our emotions, our tears of joy and sorrow, and especially of our tender feelings which harmonise with mothering and being mothered. Seeking unity by fraying personal boundaries and merging with the universal (as rivers merge into the sea) is Water's way.

Terrestrial life is only possible in a moist environment. In some primordial swamp where crucial nutrients were available (Earth), life was born and nurtured in the womb of nature under the action of light and heat (Fire). *La mer* and *Il mare* are the words for sea in French and Italian, while the words for mother, *la mère* and *la madre,* remind us of the etymological connection between sea and mother.

Some characteristics associated with elemental Earth

Elemental earth is primarily associated with bodily sensations—those who are ruled by it seek understanding by developing structures and fixing meaning. They express themselves by knowing and naming.

Earth combines two basic qualities: aridity and solidity. The image which most vividly exemplifies this is stone as used in buildings: castle, cathedral, tomb, bank or hovel. The qualities of Earth are retention and containment (as in a tomb or bank vault) and structure. Old age is also associated with Earth, as is wisdom, the vault and repository of experience. In old age the past is remembered in greatest detail, while the present may be forgotten. Wisdom which has been condensed out of this seasoned maturity is represented by the symbol of the Philosopher's Stone, The Lapis which is the goal of the alchemist's work.

Earth is also that medium which, when moist, supports vegetable life. It is noteworthy that vegetation (which is at the base of all food chains) constructs its material, cellular existence (Earth) by the process of photosynthesis. The energy of sunlight (Fire) is utilised by chloroplasts in the synthesis of Water (Water) and carbon dioxide (Air). Just as the axis of Fire/Air is of spirit, so the axis of Water/Earth is that of materiality (memory and time as well as dimensions).

An elemental map of criteria for potency selection

- Highest potencies, MM and CM, may be used in the most acute situations, such as a life and death encounter, where maximum energy must be expended for survival, no matter what the later repair cost may be to the organism. For instance, a high fever in a child may give rise to convulsions, the destruction of innumerable brain cells, in the process of vanquishing invading bacteria. This acute level of expression could be called the ASTRAL level because it represents the soul's transition between matter and spirit.

- Highest potencies also harmonise with elemental ETHER, that is, where the expression is instantly of spirit/energy in matter/body. Little children and very old people often operate at this level. This expression is completely direct and uncompensated.

- Patients who operate in an elemental FIRE mode also do best on high potencies: 10M and above. Elemental fire communicates in images; intuition is the primary *modus operandi* and as in the case of Ether, the person experiences the world spontaneously. When questioning about a thing, they want to ascertain, "Where did it came from? Where is it going?" They often view things in terms of connections, ontological enquiry and God. If they are sexually active, then this expression is direct and uncompensated. HOT and LIGHT are the key-concepts.

- Patients who operate in an elemental AIR mode do well on medium to high potencies: 200c to 10M. Elemental air is primarily associated with thinking—seeking knowledge by processes of discrimination and division. They often ask, "What is it? How can I understand it?" They usually view things in terms of ideas and theoretical enquiry. The dark side of elemental air, because it operates by division and subtraction (from the elemental levels of fire, where intuition unifies vision and water, where feelings may flow and harmonise), manifests with delusions of death, of separation, of the various realms of hell. COLD (as in cold reason) and DARK are key concepts.

- Patients who operate in an elemental WATER mode do well on lower potencies: 200c and below. Elemental water is primarily associated with feeling. These patients seek meaning by dissolving and merging; they exhibit alternating and varied moods and their lives are influence by their emotions. They want to ascertain, "Does it suit me or not, do I accept it or not?" LIQUID or FLUID is the key concept.

- Patients who operate in an elemental EARTH mode do well on low potencies: 30c to mother tinctures. These patients seek meaning by developing safe structures and adopting fixed attitudes. They present by knowing facts and details and by endlessly naming things. They want to ascertain, "Is it really there? Is it a fact? What is it called?" SOLID is the key concept.

Regarding modalities: marked modalities indicate a dynamic vital response, in respect of accepting or rejecting. Therefore, whichever level a patient is on, their particular potency may be raised by a level. For instance, a patient with only physical symptoms and fixed attitudes who has a very marked food aggravation and time modality, may, on the basis of this, receive a 200c potency.

The two models (checklist and elemental map) are mutually inclusive—that is, they should be used in conjunction with one another.

APPENDIX 2

HOMEOPATHIC GLOSSARY OF COMMONLY USED TERMS

Allopathy: *Allos* in Greek means 'other than', or 'different from', while pathy means suffering. *Allopathic* medicine refers to the practice of prescribing drugs, or using therapeutic techniques, according to the principle of different or other action. This is not the case with homeopathy, where healing agents are chosen specifically because they cure similar suffering. Allopathy, alongside surgery and various forms of replacement therapy, is the dominant form of medicine in the West today.

Case receiving or case taking: The process of receiving medical, personal, psychological and historically based information from a patient in order to arrive at an understanding of what needs to be cured. Listening, looking, touching and smelling come into it, as also do more subtle forms of sensing. This also involves some questioning in order to amplify and enlarge upon the information presented.

Common symptoms: Such symptoms as are typically experienced during the course of a disease or state, e.g. sharp pain in the side and shallow breathing during pleurisy, or weeping after recent grief. These symptoms rank least important when prescribing homeopathically because they do not shed light upon the uniqueness of the suffering individual: they are common to the diseased state.

Constitution (or Diathesis): The general condition and health of the individual as determined by such factors as heredity and *miasms,* life history, lifestyle, environment, and past treatments. (See **Miasms**)

Constitutional treatment: Treatment that is aimed at strengthening an individual's characteristic make-up and mental character and hence their ability to protect themselves against diseases. A constitutional prescription aims to stimulate the whole organism's regenerative powers. Homeopaths arrive at such prescriptions by virtue of a detailed analysis of emotional, mental and physical aspects of the whole being, (totality) rather than by prescribing on the disease's smaller sub-totality.

Cure: A profound overall improvement in health evidenced by the individuals heightened awareness as well as the removal of the symptoms of the disease. (See **Health**)

Drug Picture: A summary of symptoms, emotional, mental and physical, including pathological tissue changes that a medicinal substance is capable of causing (and curing) in human beings. Reference to the substance's signature, mythology, use, and other anecdotal material may be given, as well as case examples. (See **Signature**)

Dynamis: energy, life-force, power (to manifest).

Epidemic: A disease that affects large numbers of individuals in one place and at one time; an infectious disease which spreads rapidly, overwhelming many.

Essence: That which constitutes the being of a thing. 'That by which it is what it is'. This describes one of the pathways of remedy selection, according to matching the remedy's inner, essential nature, to the inner nature of the patient.

General Symptoms: Symptoms that pertain to the person as a whole, including all psychical symptoms and such physical symptoms as affect the whole being (as distinct from *particular symptoms,* i.e. those which affect the parts). *General symptoms,* e.g. wakefulness after 3 am, worse from sunshine, anger from contradiction, are of the greatest value to the physician because they represent the organism's overall response to the imbalance. (See **Hierarchy of symptoms**)

Genus epidemicus: The most commonly prescribed remedy(s) in an epidemic, e.g. Camphora, Cuprum or Veratrum album in cholera, or Gelsemium in influenza. In practice, the *genus epidemicus* is usually discovered retrospectively on the basis of a statistical analysis of common denominator symptoms: it is therefore only available for those affected by the next occurrence of a similar epidemic.

Hahnemann, Samuel: The founder of homeopathy as we know it today, born 13 April 1755 in Meissen, Saxony, died 2 July 1843.

Healing crisis: The initial response to the stimulus of the remedy is a vital one in which the organism is energised. Since the stimulus provided by the administration of the *simillimum* is 'in tune' with the symptoms of the disease (it is selected precisely because it matches them) the initial effect is one of aggravation: the symptoms are intensified. In the case of acute disease the aggravation of presenting symptoms is often so brief as to pass unnoticed, while in the case of chronic disease it may continue for days, or, in exceptional cases weeks. After this initial period, an amelioration of the symptoms occurs together with an increased sense of wellbeing, a whole or partial cure in other words. In the case of the treatment of chronic disease the period of aggravation may be followed by further stages in the process of healing; this following the progress of Hering's law of cure.

Health: Health may be described as the organism's ability to adapt itself to changing circumstances while maintaining its integrity. The process of adaptation, providing it is successful, leads to strength, 'the lessons of experience' being manifest not only in the body, but also in the realisation of formerly latent creativity. Health may be understood to imply freedom from rigidity of body, emotions and mind and is associated with a rhythmic and unbounded flow of vitality such as we may witness in children and certain wise old people.

Hering's Law of Cure: First described by the homeopath Constantine Hering (1800-1880), these observations describe the changes which occur during the curative process. These responses to the healing agency are the accepted bench mark by which all therapists (no matter which discipline they follow) may assess the progress of their patients. These trends when reversed tend towards morbidity. The three components of Hering's Law are:

1) Healing proceeds from the innermost of the organism and extends outwards, disease being removed from those organs without which survival would be impossible towards less vital and peripheral organs, e.g. nervous system pathology such as locomotor ataxia to skin pathology such as generalised eczema, or, to cite a psychologically based example, from claustrophobia to catharsis and weeping, being the release from the 'locked up' memory of past grief. This example leads to:

2) Healing proceeds in reverse order of the symptom's appearance; that the first disease symptoms to have appeared will be the last to be cured, and that the last to have appeared will be the first to be cured.

3) Healing follows a downward course, from head to foot, or from trunk to extremities. The course of externalisation of disease is via the shortest 'venting' route, for example, breast lumps disappear and there is increase axillary sweating.

Hierarchy of symptoms: For the purposes of analysis, according to J.T.Kent, the totality of a patient's symptoms are organised into a hierarchy of relative importance such that most weight is given to *mental general* symptoms (psychical symptoms), and least to *physical particular* symptoms, i.e. those relating to the suffering of the parts.

Homeopathy: The restoration of the sick to health by means of the application of the law of similars. Introduced to the world by Samuel Hahnemann in 1796.

Homeostasis: A state of dynamic equilibrium. In the living body this is maintained by the *vital force* and by its agency the *defence mechanism.* This ensures that such forces as tend to disorganise are balanced by forces which maintain integrity of structure and constancy of function. A loss of homeostasis is evidenced by the production of the signs and symptoms of disease; these range from the mildest disturbances, such as transient loss of acumen, or headache, to chronic disorders. Death follows in the wake of a total breakdown of the *defence mechanism.*

Iatrogenic: An effect created by the physician, either by the power of suggestion, for instance, by giving a diagnosis with a gloomy prognosis, or by the drugs prescribed.

Law of similars: Stated by the ancients and again by Paracelsus (1495-1541) this principle was given an empirical basis in the field of therapeutics by Samuel Hahnemann. In Latin the law is stated *similia similibus curantur,* 'like is cured by like'. Its therapeutic application states that a substance which causes symptoms to occur when given to healthy subjects (see **Provings**) acts as a curative medicine when given to sick persons exhibiting similar symptoms.

Materia medica: Latin for 'materials of medicines'. This is a text book listing remedies, their sources, preparation and detailed indications of their usage. The source material is derived from the provings (experiments) upon healthy volunteers as well as from verified clinical observation. (See **Provings**)

Miasms: A theory developed by Samuel Hahnemann after twelve years of practice and observation. It states that there are three fundamental disorganisations of the vital force, that they are acquired and transmitted genetically and that they are, either singly, or more commonly in combination, responsible for the ills of mankind. Further, Hahnemann states that the miasms were generated by the suppression of disease by our ancestors. Suppressed skin eruptions, scabies in particular, being responsible for the creation of the first, most basic and 'hydra headed' of the miasms:

> *Psora.* This miasm is characterised by 'the itch', by dryness and de-animation of the skin and mucous membranes, by hypo-function in general, and hence lack of vital heat, by general anxieties, loss of self confidence and slowness of mental functions.

> *Syphilis* is responsible for its own miasm, typified by destructive tendencies upon all levels of the being, necrosis of tissues, haemorrhage; mental hallmarks being suicide as well as murder.

> *Sycosis* is the third miasm and refers to the propensity by the organism to neoplasms. Over-activity in general is characteristic, expressed by wetness of mucous membranes (and aggravation from damp); persons demanding affection and approbation, suffering from emotional instability and neediness, acquisitiveness, insatiability, and superabundance of ideas.

It is worthy of note that the three miasms express the same 'roots of suffering' as described by 'illusion and ignorance', 'aversion and hatred', 'desire and greed'.

Modality: A circumstance that makes a person's health, or a specific symptom, either better, or worse. For example 'I feel better in the mountains'; 'My chilblains are better for the fresh air'; 'I feel suicidal in the moonlight'; 'My stomach feels empty at eleven a.m.'; 'I am more energetic after midnight.'

Morbific: That which causes disease, i.e. a destructive agent which, either temporarily or permanently, affects the organism. The effect of the *morbific* influence will depend upon 1) its virulence and 2) the strength or weakness of the organism. This in turn is dependent upon such factors as heredity (*miasmatic* background) and maintaining causes such as diet, sanitation, emotional wellbeing and attitude.

Nosode: A homeopathically prepared potency of a diseased organ, or of a disease product. Hahnemann, for example, created the remedy *Psorinum* from the pus of a scabies vesicle; the remedy *Tuberculinum bovinum* is prepared from the lymph glands of tubercular cattle.

Organism: A living being. An organised body, consisting of interconnected and mutually dependent parts constituted to share a common life.

Polycrest remedy: A remedy which in its provings produces changes in all parts of the organism and which is therefore well known and for which a detailed description is provided. A remedy with a wide range of clinical applications.

Potency and Potentisation: Potency refers to the power and influence of the medicine. The object of a prescription is to effect maximum benefit for minimum effort, above all to leave the organism unaffected by possibly noxious side effects of the dose. This is achieved by reducing the mass while simultaneously increasing the energy. The method involves subjecting the substance to serial dilution and succussion (vibration, or banging), or in the case of insoluble substances, trituration, or grinding. These steps have the effect of liberating the medicinal activity, while at the same time reducing the mass and consequently possible iatrogenic affects. The process may be carried out with a dilution constant of one-in-ten: decimal scale, designated by the suffix 'x', or, with a dilution constant of one-in-one hundred: centesimal scale, designated by the suffix 'c', or one-in-50,000: LM scale. For example, a potency of 30c implies that the original material (in the case of a plant extract, the *mother tincture.*) has been submitted to 30 successive dilutions of one-in-one hundred, each stage having been energised by succussion.

Psyche: Greek for breath, soul, life (as distinct from the body), used to refer to both conscious and subconscious mind. Hence **psychical:** of, or pertaining to the psyche, **psychology:** the study of the psyche, and **psychosomatic:** corporal manifestations of psychic origin.

Proving: The testing of a medicinal substance, either in potentised or crude form, upon healthy subjects (the provers). The provers are instructed to take detailed notes of any deviations from the norm which they experience; this may span an extended period. The physician in attendance adds objective symptoms, and the amassed information, subjective and in the language of the prover, as well as objective and in the language of the physician, is arranged into a schema in the homeopathic materia medica. In this manner new material is continuously being added to the texts.

Repertory: Literally an inventory, or storehouse where things may be found. The homeopathic repertory is an index of drug symptoms, each heading, or rubric listing those drugs known to cause and cure that symptom. The remedies are listed to show prominence, from the most frequently occurring in the provings, marked by printing in bold, black type, through italic to small type. Hence the phrase, 'bold type symptom' is used to denote a major characteristic of a remedy's pathogenesis.

Rubric: A listing of remedies found in a homeopathic repertory. These listings are under the heading of a symptom, a sign or a disease, such as: Mind, hurried, in movements; Mind, ailments from grief; Face, freckles; Generalities, diabetes.

Sarcode: *Sarcodes* are usually grouped with nosodes because they are potencies derived from organs and secretions. However these are from healthy sources (unlike the diseased organs and products used in the production of nosodes), and include such remedies as *thyroidinum* and *lumbar disci.*

Signature: The doctrine of signatures states that the shape and form of a substance yields evidence of its medicinal activity. To this may be added related stories or myths and the uses, commercial, artistic or scientific, to which the substance is put.

Simillimum: The one medicine which most closely matches the patient's uniqueness at a given point in time as described by their totality of characteristic symptoms.

Soma: Greek for body.

Somatic: of, or pertaining to the body.

Susceptibility: The capacity of being affected by morbific influences— 'the weak spot'. The aim of treatment of chronic cases is to reduce susceptibility to disease.

Symptoms: Either objective, or subjective changes in the physical, mental, or emotional condition of an individual that limit freedom.

Symptom generation: It is understood that symptoms represent efforts by the organism to deal with either internal or external stress; they represent the most successful adaptation, that is to say they prevent the disturbance from striking inwards (centripetally) and allowing a more grave situation to develop. Ref. paragraph 201 in Hahnemann's *Organon of Medicine*.

Temperament: Natural disposition and physical constitution. The categorisation of the four temperaments has its roots in ancient Greece. The fluidic, feminine aspects of the psyche express in *Sanguine* and *Phlegmatic* temperaments, while the structured, masculine aspect express in *Choleric* and *Melancholic* temperaments. The descriptive totality of the temperaments includes all levels of being as well as characteristic pathology. By way of example we may cite the *Choleric* constitution which inclines the individual to be forceful, astute and zealous in health, but in disease inclines towards destructive irritability, even suicidal disposition with somatic focus to the heart, arterial circulation, liver and digestive tract.

Tincture: Remedies in liquid form, usually of plant origin, made with a mixture of ethyl alcohol and water as a solvent. The raw extract is called 'mother tincture', designated by ø, and it is from this that the potencies are made by serial dilution and succussion. (See **Potency** and **Potentisation**)

Vaccinosis: A state of chronic ill health which may follow after vaccination and/or inoculation. This is explained by the *defence mechanism* being partially 'tied up' in a response to the injected disease serum. Because the *immune* capacity becomes committed to the inoculated disease, it is not available to counteract other contagions. Based upon the evidence of clinical experience, the homeopathic practitioner knows that a proportion of patients, at some point during their treatment, respond better to remedies after the taint of inoculation has been counteracted by the administration of a specific, often *isopathic* remedy. Furthermore, it is not uncommon for the *simillimum* to temporarily 'reawaken' an old vaccination scar (manifesting itching and erythema) during a *healing crisis* and by these means eliminating the taint and restoring health.

Vital force: "In the healthy condition of man, the spiritual vital force is the dynamis that animates the material body, which rules with unbounded sway and retains all the parts of the organism in admirable, harmonious, vital operation, as regards both sensations and functions, so that our indwelling, reason gifted mind can freely employ this living, healthy instrument for the higher purposes of our existence. The material body, without the vital force, is capable of no sensation, no function, no self preservation; it is dead and now only subject to the power of the external physical world; it decays and is again resolved into its chemical constituents." From paragraphs 9 and 10 in the *Organon of Medicine* by Hahnemann.